Orientation and Mobility:
Techniques for Independence

The publication of this book was supported by a grant from
The Royal New Zealand Foundation for the Blind

Orientation and Mobility: Techniques for Independence

Steven J. LaGrow
Massey University

Marvin J. Weessies
Western Michigan University

The Dunmore Press Ltd

©1994 Steven J. LaGrow and Marvin J. Weessies
©1994 The Dunmore Press Limited

First Published in 1994
for the authors by
The Dunmore Press Limited
P.O.Box 5115
Palmerston North
New Zealand

ISBN 086469 172 6

Illustrations by Kathleen Newman

Text: New Century Schoolbook 10.5/12.5
Printer: Dunmore Printing Company Ltd.
Palmerston North

Table of Contents

Introduction

A limitation on independent movement is one of the most basic handicaps faced by blind and visually impaired people. Independent movement requires skill in both orientation and mobility.

Orientation refers to the ability to establish and maintain an awareness of one's position in space and is dependent upon both the gathering and interpretation of available sensory information. This information may be visual, auditory, kinesthetic, tactile, thermal and/or olfactory. Successful interpretation of sensory cues is dependent upon a known and predictable environment. Visually impaired travelers are taught to recognize and anticipate the regularities of the environments in which they travel. Exceptions to those regularities become more informative than the regularities themselves. They become landmarks which a traveler can use to pinpoint his or her exact location in space (Hill & Ponder, 1976). None of this is achievable, however, without mobility.

Mobility refers to the act of moving through space in a safe and efficient manner. The traveler should not be expected to attend to sensory input and environmental layout when safety is not assured. Primary mobility devices, including human guides, long canes and dog guides, enable the traveler to move with safety. In addition to safety, the non-visual traveler must be able to establish and maintain a straight line, successfully perform and recognize changes in direction, circumvent objects in the path of travel while maintaining a basic line of travel, and recover from veers and other unintended or unexpected changes in direction.

The techniques, aids and instructional strategies used for orientation and mobility (O&M) may vary greatly depending upon the goals set for instruction and the needs and abilities of those for whom the service is provided (Uslan, Hill & Peck, 1989). The amount of vision one has, for example, may have an impact on the methods and techniques used to gain independence in travel (Dodds & Davis, 1989; Hall, Bailey, Kekelis, Raasch & Goodrich, 1987; Long, Reiser & Hill, 1990), as could the individual's age (Hill & Hill, 1991; Joffee, 1988; LaGrow & Blasch, 1992; Long, McNeal & Griffin-Shirley, 1990; Pogrund & Rosen, 1989; Skellinger & Hill, 1991) and sensory, cognitive, spatial and physical capability (Chen & Smith, 1992; Gee, Harrell & Rosenberg, 1987; Harley, Long, Merbler & Wood, 1987; Joffee, 1989; Joffee & Rikhye, 1991; Rikhye, Gothelf & Appell, 1989).

The goals of instruction may be set anywhere along a continuum from simple route travel to the complex task of independent travel in unfamiliar environments. These environments may be indoor or outdoor, urban or rural. Urban environments may be further specified to include residential, semi-business, and business areas. The goals of travel may be limited to specified localities or generalized across environments. The desired level of independence identifies the degree of generalization expected.

Route travelers, for example, are taught a specific route to and from a given destination and the skills required to complete it. They are not expected to generalize skills across other routes or to select alternative routes of travel.

Independent travelers, on the other hand, conceptualize the environment of travel by generalizing the rules of layout within and across environments. They are not taught specific routes of travel. Rather, they are expected to plan routes of travel independently to various locations from different starting points and select alternative routes when required. They are expected to generalize across environments, including unfamiliar ones.

This book describes the techniques and instructional strategies used to enable an adventitiously blinded adult (i.e., one who has experienced a loss of functional vision after having had usable vision) with no other apparent handicapping conditions, to regain independence in travel in an urban environment. As a result, a relatively complete range of the competencies involved in non-visual travel are presented (Uslan, Hill & Peck, 1989), as is an ideal instructional sequence.

The program of instruction presented here is not meant to define the field of orientation and mobility in the 1990s. Rather, it is limited to an instructional system appropriate to the needs of a significant minority of the population served by O&M instructors, of whom more than two-thirds have some degree of usable vision and half may be considered to be multiply impaired (Uslan, Hill & Peck, 1989). Many are old and have more limited goals (Long, McNeal & Griffen-Shirley, 1990), some are quite young and have other more age-appropriate goals to be addressed (Hill, Rosen, Correa & Langley, 1984), and still others have been visually impaired since birth and therefore have never experienced a loss in sight or function (Uslan, Hill & Peck, 1989). It may also serve as a basis for adaptation or modification for these others.

The first chapter explores the myriad variables which must be considered when selecting the instructional strategies used to teach orientation and mobility as part of the process of rehabilitation. Chapters 2 to 5 present the various techniques required for safe and independent travel by a functionally blind individual, including the use of human guides, self-protective and positional techniques, self-familiarization and systematic search patterns, and various cane techniques (note: instructional strategies employed to teach the use of a dog guide as a primary mobility aid is not included in this text since instruction in their use is a specialist area not normally covered by O&M instructors). Chapters 6 and 7 introduce the reader to the various environments used for instruction and propose an ideal sequence for their introduction. The final chapter deals with the use of public transportation for travel within and between cities. The role of the O&M instructor as an advocate for the user of public transit systems is also discussed.

In this text, in order to avoid the cumbersome 'he or she' reference, where we have not been able to use inclusive language we have chosen to refer to the guide as female and the traveller as male.

1

Instructional Strategies

Orientation and mobility refers to both the skills and the techniques required for independent travel and the instructional strategies used to teach them. Orientation and mobility programs were originally designed to meet the needs of young, capable, adventitiously (i.e., acquired, not present at birth) blinded veterans during and immediately following World War II (Joffee & Rikhye, 1991). These strategies were successfully introduced to congenitally (i.e., present at birth) blind children without substantial modification in the early 1960s to the surprise of many, since they were clearly designed for use with newly blinded adults (Wiener & Welsch, 1980). Their subsequent introduction in the 1970s and '80s, first to those with low vision and later to those with multiple impairments, was less successful. It became apparent that modifications to both the techniques used and the instructional strategies employed would be required if success was to be achieved. Persons with low vision, for example, had different needs in terms of aids, techniques and orientation strategies while those with multiple impairments often had different learning styles which needed accommodating (Apple, Apple & Blasch, 1980; Joffee & Rikhye, 1991).

Numerous modifications were introduced over the ensuing years making orientation and mobility instruction more appropriate for persons with diverse needs and/or ability (Uslan, Hill & Peck,

1989), including those who

(a)   have some usable vision (Apple, 1976; Dodds & Davis, 1989; Hall, Bailey, Kekelis, Raasch & Goodrich, 1987; Long, Reiser & Hill, 1990),

(b)   have other disabling conditions in addition to those resulting from a visual impairment (Chen & Smith, 1992; Gee, Harrell, & Rosenberg, 1987; Harley, Long, Merbler & Wood, 1987; Harley & Merbler, 1980; Harley, Wood & Merbler, 1980; Joffee, 1989; Joffee & Rikhye, 1991; Rikhye, Gothelf & Appell, 1989).

(c)   are very young, (Bosbach, 1988; Hill, 1984; Foy, Kirchner & Wople, 1991; Foy, Von Scheden & Waiculous, 1982; Hill, Dodson-Burk & Smith, 1989; Hill, Rosen, Correa, & Langley, 1984; Kronick, 1987; Ketterer, 1988; Pogrund & Rosen, 1989; Skellinger & Hill, 1991), and

(d)   are relatively old (Hill & Hill, 1991; Long, McNeal & Griffin-Shirley, 1990; LaGrow & Blasch, 1992; Straw, Harley & Zimmerman, 1991; Welsh, 1980),

We now realize that the techniques, aids and instructional strategies used to teach visually impaired people to travel may vary greatly depending upon the goals set for instruction and the needs and abilities of the individual for whom instruction is provided. As a result, every program of instruction should be individualized to reflect the uniqueness of each person served.

INDIVIDUALIZATION

'Individualization of any program of instruction relies upon (a) a thorough and on-going system of evaluation, (b) a specific plan of action tailored to the needs and desires of the individual to be served, and (c) a flexible delivery system available for the provision of service' (LaGrow, 1992, p.99). This process begins with a thorough evaluation of the individual and the social/cultural and physical environment in which he lives (Vander Kolk, 1981).

Evaluation

The purpose of the initial evaluation is to develop an understanding of and rapport with the person to be served, determine his or her needs and desires in relation to orientation and mobility training, and identify the level at which the person is currently functioning. This information is required before goals can be set and an instructional plan developed.

Comprehensive View of the Individual Served

Information is gathered from a number of sources, including the person in question and/or family members in order to develop a comprehensive view of the individual to be served. Medical, psychological, social, economic and vocational information is commonly obtained (Wright, 1972). This information is usually required by a number of specialists for planning purposes (e.g. case manager, counselor, occupational therapist, physical therapist, low-vision specialist, recreational specialist, rehabilitation teacher, social worker, vocational evaluator, etc.). To avoid duplication, it is often gathered by a single agent (e.g., social worker/case manager) as part of the intake process.

Medical examinations or reports are obtained to determine the extent and nature of the impairment, ensure that all ophthalmological and optometric needs have been met, and determine the overall health of the individual in question. General health status is ascertained, as the increase in activity usually associated with O&M instruction could pose a serious health threat to some. General assessments are also conducted to identify the presence of other disabling conditions. As a result, medical evaluations may also include secondary assessments by nurses, physical therapists, dietitians (e.g., for those with diabetes), psychologists (e.g., for those who have experienced a head injury) and audiologists.

Psychological evaluations may be ordered to determine if the individual is ready to begin the rehabilitation process. A loss of vision, like any other significant loss, requires time to mourn, to deny, to be angry and finally to accept and adjust to (Mishkin, 1988). This is a normal process which the individual should be given the time to go through before a comprehensive rehabilitation program is begun (LaGrow, 1992). However, psychological adjustment should not be seen as something that is to be completed before any instruction begins. Rather, it ought to be viewed as a continuous process of coping (Beggs, 1992) which may be aided by experiencing success in mobility, interacting with others in the rehabilitation process, and/or through group or individual counseling (Dale, 1992).

Social histories are taken to identify those factors which are important to the individual, to recognize value systems, socio-cultural patterns and personal and familial inter-relationships. The attitudes, perceptions and behaviors of family and friends can have a significant impact on the success achieved within the rehabilitation process (Dale, 1992; Dumas & Sadowsky, 1984; Moore, 1984; Ponchillia, 1984).

Economic and vocational information may be obtained to better understand the individual to be served, while at the same time insuring that all economic needs of the family have been met to allow the individual to concentrate on the rehabilitation process (LaGrow, 1992).

Needs and Desires

One's needs and desires are highly personal matters and are dependent upon a myriad of factors. These factors are influenced by age, ability and the environment in which one lives. Young children, for example, have a need to get out and move, to explore environments and develop body, spatial and environmental concepts. Their needs correspond to their developmental level. Their range of travel is constrained by their maturity and their parents' perception of the degree to which they may be trusted on their own.

Visually impaired children have age appropriate needs. Those needs may be identified by observing their normally sighted peers. Visually impaired adolescents, however, may have their need for independent travel accelerated in anticipation of the leap in independence their normally sighted peers will experience when they reach the age to obtain a driver's license.

Working age people need to get to work, to get about at work and to care for themselves, their homes and their family's needs. They often have a need to generalize their travel skills over numerous environments. It may be expected that these people will move several times in their lives. Each time they move, they will have to get used to a new place of residence, neighborhood and often town or city.

Older people may be more settled in their choice of residence and thus have more need for environmental specific travel and less need for generalized skill. They also tend to travel outside of their homes by themselves less frequently than do younger people (Long, McNeal & Griffin-Shirley, 1990).

The difference in the frequency of travel across age groups may reflect a difference in ability as much as it does a difference in need. Older visually impaired persons tend to have more secondary disabilities than their younger counterparts (LaGrow & Blasch, 1992). However, the presence of other disabling conditions will affect mobility needs regardless of age.

Although those with multiple impairments have the same need to move safely and independently about their environment (Joffee & Rikhye, 1991), they often have different requirements imposed upon them by their disabilities (Florence & LaGrow, 1989; Rikhye, Gothelf & Appell, 1989; Rowland & Schweight, 1990).

Variations in cognitive and sensory ability may affect the way in which orientation and mobility is taught (Gee, Harrell & Rosenberg, 1987), as well as the content of that instruction. Mentally retarded travelers, for example, may be restricted to familiar environments and/or route travel due to difficulty with generalization no matter how much vision they have available for travel (LaGrow, Wiener & LaDuke, 1990). A hearing loss, on the other hand, may affect the types of intersections one can utilize to safely cross streets.

A hearing loss resulting in an inability to gain orientation by traffic sounds, for example, may force the individual to avoid quiet residential crossings in favor of busier intersections where aid in determining the time to cross may be obtained (Florence & LaGrow, 1989). Thus, these travelers may have a greater need for route planning than others.

Persons with low vision may or may not require instruction in the use of the long cane, illumination control devices, and/or distance aids (Hall, Bailey, Kekelis, Raasch & Goodrich, 1987; Smith, De l'Aune & Geruschat, 1992). The type of loss may have more affect on need than the degree of loss. A loss in field or contrast sensitivity, for example, is more likely to restrict mobility than a loss in acuity (Long, Reiser & Hill, 1990).

Travel needs will also be affected by the environment in which a person lives. Simple things, like the presence of sidewalks (footpaths) outside a person's residence may contribute to the amount of travel he does (Long, McNeal & Griffin-Shirley, 1990). The availability and locality of pedestrian crossings and bus stops can have a significant effect on the opportunity for independent travel, as can the perceived safety of the environment in which the individual anticipates travelling. Urban environments in some countries are simply not conducive to independent travel: the sidewalks are overcrowded and used by vendors or vehicles, traffic may move in almost any direction and open sewage systems may run along the footpath (Taheri-Araghi, 1992). Others provide tremendous opportunity through public transit systems (Eames & Eames, 1990). In fact, in numerous cities, it is more convenient to travel by public transport than by private car.

Smaller towns and rural environments impose certain restrictions on travel and therefore affect individual need. For example, some areas have no public transit systems, pedestrian-controlled intersections, sidewalks, or even paved streets.

The individual's needs and desires are often identified early as the instructor seeks to build rapport and establish goals for instruction. They are identified by both interview and direct observation which is carried out as part of the functional evaluation. The instructor's perception, however, may change as skill and confidence is gained during the instructional phase of the program. As a result, the program must remain flexible in order to respond to such changes.

Current Level of Function

The manner in which functional evaluations are carried out is dependent upon the individual's need for generalizing skills across environments. If the person's needs are restricted to route travel within a specific environment, for example, that environment and the travel routes within it are analyzed to identify the specific skills required to travel those particular routes. The person is then observed travelling within or along those routes to determine his current level of functioning, the skills which must be taught to reach the goals of instruction, where instruction is to begin, and which sensory clues may be relied upon at specific junctures within those routes. If, however, his needs include generalization of skills across environments then a more general approach to evaluation is taken.

In this case, functional evaluations are conducted to identify the person's current level of function, understanding of environmental regularities, and use of visual, auditory, tactile, and kinesthetic (i.e., sense of movement) senses. These evaluations depend upon direct observation of the individual travelling in a number of situations.

Evaluations are conducted in the actual environments of travel at different times of day and night to observe the effects of various visual conditions on a person's functional ability. Environments which contain a variety of terrain, textural and auditory information are selected for sampling the individual's response to diverse input. Students are asked to travel in environments of varying complexity and familiarity to identify their understanding of these environments (i.e., indoor, residential, semi-business,

business, rural, malls and plazas), and to determine their ability to generalize across them. They are also exposed to different types of intersections (i.e., T, off-set, roundabouts), streets (i.e., one-way, two-way, two-lane, four-lane) and methods of traffic control (i.e., myriad lights and signs) to ascertain their ability to recognize and cope with these differences as well.

Environments and tasks are introduced in such a way that increasingly complex travel skills are required. The evaluation process continues until deficits in skill, ability or understanding are identified and a starting point for instruction is established.

Establishing Goals and Planning Programs

Once the individual's needs, desires, abilities, and current level of functioning have been identified, the goals and objectives of the instructional program can be set. The program to be provided is thus defined and specified.

Establishing the Goal of Instruction

Goals should be realistic statements of expected achievement which reflect the purpose for the provision of the service in terms of both the levels of independence to be attained and the type of environment in which this will be realized. The level at which the goal is set is variable and is dependent upon ability, motivation, desire, need, and time allocated.

Goals may be established for route, semi-independent or independent travel in familiar or unfamiliar environments. These environments may be indoor or outdoor, urban or rural. Urban environments may be further specified to include residential, semi-business, and business areas.

The goals of travel may be limited to specified localities or be intended to be generalized across environments. The level of independence set identifies the degree of generalization expected.

Route travelers are not expected to generalize the skills obtained beyond the environments of travel. They are taught a specific route to and from a given destination and the skills required to complete it. They are not expected to generalize skills across other routes or to select alternative routes of travel. Route travelers would not be expected to travel alone in unfamiliar environments.

Semi-independent travelers are taught routes as well, but are expected to generalize skills from route to route. These travelers learn and use recovery strategies when they are lost or disoriented, and may detour if necessary. They may be expected to generalize skills across environments following familiarization with the environment in question.

Independent travelers conceptualize the environment of travel by generalizing rules of layout within and across environments. They are not taught specific routes of travel. Rather, they are expected to plan routes of travel independently to various locations from different starting points and select alternative routes when required. They are expected to generalize across environments and may be expected to do so to travel in unfamiliar environments as well (i.e., for those with the goal of independent travel in unfamiliar environments).

The level of independence set is often situational. For example, a person may desire to become an independent traveler in a familiar indoor, residential and semi-business environment, a semi-independent traveler in a familiar business environment and a route traveler when using a public transit system. If this is the case, multiple goals are established.

Intermediate Objectives

Each goal is defined by a series of intermediate objectives. 'Intermediate objectives are statements of short-term achievement which, when put in chronological order, logically bridge the gap from the current level of functioning to the instructional goal' (LaGrow, 1992, p. 112). The objectives, then, reflect the increments of skill required to achieve the goal. They also contain the criteria and conditions under which those skills will be evaluated. As a result, they must be both observable and measurable (Thomson, Brown, Chapman, Benson & Pine, 1991).

The criteria for determining if an objective has been met indicates the degree of competence the instructor requires to be demonstrated before moving on to the next objective. The conditions for evaluation identify the circumstances under which the skill will be demonstrated. The condition statement usually includes a description of the instructions provided, the mobility aids employed and the environment in which the skill will be performed. For example, the goal of independent travel in a familiar business environment for an individual who is currently relying on the use of a human guide for all outdoor travel may have to progress from indoor, through residential and semi-business travel to business travel to meet this goal. Therefore, the short-term objectives would be reflective of this progression.

These objectives may be stated as follows:

Objective 1: On two consecutive days the student will locate three objectives within a familiar indoor environment when given the room numbers only, while traveling independently with the use of the long cane, without prompt or assistance.

Objective 2: On two consecutive days the student will locate three objectives within a familiar residential environment when given the addresses only, while traveling independently with the use of the long cane, without prompt or assistance.

Objective 3: On three consecutive days the student will locate a specific business within a familiar semi-business area when given the name of the business only, while traveling independently with the use of the long cane, without prompt or assistance from the instructor.

Objective 4: On three consecutive days the student will locate three businesses within a familiar business environment when given the name of the business and responses to his structured questions, without prompt or assistance.

As can be seen from this example, the objectives plot the progress expected from the current level of functioning to the goal for instruction. The last objective reflects the goal of instruction and may be used to determine when the goal has been reached. Each objective contains the conditions under which the individual is expected to perform and the criteria used for evaluation. The objectives identify the skills which epitomize the level of functioning desired, but do not necessarily enumerate all the skills required.

The example used here requires the individual to identify and locate specific destinations independently across environments of varying complexity. Since independent travel is specified, we would expect the individual to plan the routes to be used, to locate the rooms, residences or businesses in question, maintain orientation while doing so, and recover if disoriented or off track. The particular travel skills and/or mobility aids required to do this are determined by the individual's needs and the actual environments of travel.

Mobility may be facilitated by the use of both primary and secondary mobility techniques and/or travel aids. Primary mobility techniques provide complete protection and coverage to the non-visual traveler. Primary techniques include the use of a human guide, dog guide and the constant-contact and touch techniques with a specially prescribed long cane. Secondary mobility aids and travel techniques provide supplementary information or partial coverage but do not provide complete protection from the environment by themselves. Secondary mobility techniques and/or aids include self-protective and directional techniques, the diagonal cane technique, and all electronic travel aids (ETAs) with the exception of the Laser Cane. ETAs emit high electromagnetic (i.e. laser) beams or high frequency auditory waves to 'sense' the environment. These are then reflected from objects in the travel path, received by the device and converted to an audible or a tactual signal the user perceives and interprets (Blasch, Long & Griffin-Shirley, 1989, p.449).

A functionally blind individual would be required to use either the touch or constant-contact technique for protection and various trailing techniques to locate the designated rooms, residences and businesses. Some low-vision travelers, on the other hand, may not require cane techniques, or a diagonal cane technique only. Rooms, house numbers and businesses may be located visually, either aided or unaided.

We would expect the traveler to encounter stairways, sidewalks of various widths, open spaces, a variety of streets and intersections, a number of traffic/pedestrian control devices, and numerous clues and landmarks when travelling the range of environments specified. The environmental features actually encountered, however, will depend upon the place of instruction (e.g., Peoria or Chicago, Armidale or Melbourne, Palmerston North or Auckland).

The objectives set reflect the range of skills required to meet the goals of instruction. Therefore, limited goals must be delineated as thoroughly as grand ones. For example, if a mobility goal for a child is to travel independently to and from school using a particular route, then the objectives must reflect the increments of skill required to accomplish that goal. In this case, the actual route would be delineated by the objectives as well. Thus, if the route required the student to travel along a number of discrete segments (e.g., east on Ferguson to Hereford, south on Hereford to College, east on College to the lights at Fitzherbert and then continue east on College to the pedestrian crossing at Ada and College to cross to the school), we would most likely set the objectives of the training program to correspond to mastery of each. The criteria for evaluation are variable, as explained above.

These objectives may be stated as follows:

Objective 1: The student will travel from home to the northeast corner of College and Hereford and return using the long cane on three consecutive occasions without prompt or assistance from the instructor.

Objective 2: The student will travel from home to the northwest corner of College and Fitzherbert and return using the long cane on three consecutive occasions without prompt or assistance from the instructor.

Objective 3: The student will travel from home to the school on the southeast corner of College and Ada and return using the long cane on five consecutive occasions without prompt or assistance from the instructor.

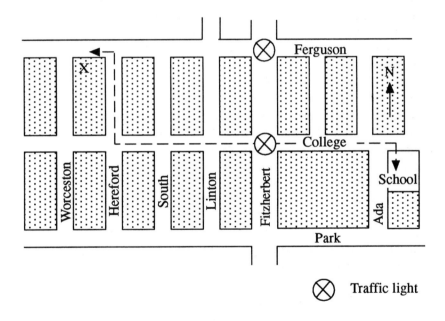

As before, the objectives plot the progression required to move from the current level of functioning to completion of the goal.

With the last objective achieved, the goal becomes operational. The actual skills required to complete these objectives are again not delineated.

In this example, a functionally blind student would have to use the touch technique or the constant-contact technique for protection, the two-point trailing technique to find certain intersecting sidewalks, the three-point trailing technique for recovery from veers when crossing streets, and the touch-and-drag for locating the pedestrian crossing at Ada. The student would be required to cross a number of residential streets without traffic controls, Fitzherbert at a traffic light which contains a pedestrian buzzer, and College at a guard-controlled pedestrian crossing at Ada and College. Other skills may be taught if the student in question is to do this at a semi-independent level.

The actual skills required, identified during the evaluation process, are delineated in the instructor's lesson plans, as are the instructional strategies employed. Other information, such as the amount of time required to reach the objective, the date by which the objective should be completed, the aids or appliances required to complete the objectives and the actual hours of instruction per week are included in the objectives themselves (LaGrow, 1992; Thomson, Brown, Chapman, Benson & Pine, 1991).

Instructional Strategies

Orientation and mobility is usually taught using a combination of direct instruction and various behavioral strategies. The mix of the two varies according to the abilities of the individual being taught, the goals set for instruction, and the setting or environment in which instruction will take place.

Direct instruction is used with those who understand the instructions given and the rationale behind them. It relies upon a shared and mutual understanding of the goals of instruction and the means for assessing them. The 'essential elements of direct instruction are systematic assessment of behavior, careful planning of instruction with regard for the identification of prerequisite skills, and the use of objective evaluation procedures so it is clear when instructional goals have been achieved. Careful sequencing and pacing of instructional activities are also ingredients of successful direct instruction' (Ward, 1986, p. 231), as is control over the instructional setting.

Behavioral strategies also rely upon careful and precise observation of behavior. These procedures are dependent upon the control of antecedents and/or consequences to maintain or modify particular behaviors (Ward, 1986). Although a shared understanding of the goals and objectives of intervention is often helpful, it is not essential to the success of these procedures. Thus, they are often relied upon when the essential elements of direct instruction cannot be met. Behavioral procedures or principles commonly employed in O&M include reinforcement, prompting, fading, shaping, and chaining (LaGrow & Leung, 1990).

Reinforcement requires the arrangement of events which results in the increase in or maintenance of a behavior (Sulzer-Azaroff & Mayer, 1991). In mobility, we use success in travel and instructor praise as primary means of reinforcement. Positive reinforcement (i.e., reinforcement delivered following an event) provides the student with feedback concerning the quality of their performance. Feedback is generally used to develop an understanding of and confidence in auditory, kinesthetic, proprioceptive and visual processing as it relates to mobility (LaGrow, 1989).

Prompts may also be used to provide the student with feedback (i.e., a verbal reminder to stay in step), or may be built into instructional programs to help with the acquisition of a behavior or behavioral chain and then faded as the student gains proficiency (LaGrow, 1989).

Fading refers to the gradual and planned removal of prompts, feedback, physical guidance or other aids which are artificially present to foster learning (Sulzer-Azaroff & Mayer, 1991). 'In mobility, instructor support, in terms of reinforcement and feedback is faded from almost continuous interaction as each sub-skill is introduced to an intermittent schedule with infrequent interaction as the sub-skill reaches mastery. Finally, the instructor removes him or herself entirely, either physically or de facto, from the scene while the student travels independently' (LaGrow, 1989, p.8).

Shaping involves the systematic reinforcement of successive approximations of a behavior as it evolves towards the objective (Sulzer-Azaroff & Mayer, 1991). Successive approximations refer to a series of behavioral elements or levels of performance in which each successive level more closely resembles the desired behavior. As a result, when shaping, we reinforce the individual only when they are performing to or better than the level expected. The level of expectation is systematically changed as skill is gained.

Chaining is a procedure whereby two or more behaviors which occur in a definite order are reinforced in sequence to establish a more complex behavior (Sulzer-Azaroff & Mayer, 1991). Routes are often taught in this manner. The route is developed in segments (e.g., as illustrated earlier using intermediate objectives) and the completion of each segment of a route becomes the stimulus for carrying out the next segment (e.g., when reaching the southeast corner of Ferguson and Hereford, travel south on Hereford to the northeast corner of College and Hereford).

These procedures, regularly used to develop specific travel skills, may also be used more extensively to teach persons with special needs. Physical positioning and prompts may also be used when teaching mobility to those who do not respond well to verbal explanations (Joffee & Rikhye, 1991). The use of these procedures and a reliance on rote routes for maintaining orientation have proven successful for persons with severe multiple disabilities who appear to have neither the conceptual or sensory prerequisites for travel (Gee & Goetz, 1985 cited in Joffee & Rikhye, 1991) and preschool children who have reached neither the developmental nor cognitive level once thought necessary for the acquisition of mobility skills (Pogrund & Rosen, 1989).

Delivery Systems

Delivery systems may be thought of as both the system of instruction employed and the setting in which it is delivered. Both must be flexible for a truly individualized program to be provided.

Orientation and mobility instruction is usually delivered to adults as either a home-based or center-based service. Children are likely to receive instruction in both the school and home environment (Bryan, 1989).

Home-based instruction allows for the delivery of environmentally specific instruction, as does school-based programming. Such instruction does not require generalization and is obviously appropriate for those who are route travelers or have environmentally specific goals. Providing instruction in any other setting would prove to be less than satisfactory.

Center-based programs, on the other hand, are more suited to the provision of instruction designed to promote generalization since the environments for instruction may be selected for their value in teaching particular concepts and skills without regard for the immediate surroundings (LaGrow, 1992). As such, center-based instruction may prove to be the most appropriate choice for those who wish to become independent travelers across a variety of environments. This is especially true for those who live in rural areas.

Most people, however, appear to require a bit of both. They either have mixed goals for travel or tend to function at the semi-independent level. Thus, they can generalize skills across some, but not all environments. A degree of flexibility is therefore required from the service provider in order to meet the individual's goals. One cannot allow the model of service delivery to determine the content of the program.

TEACHING ADVENTITIOUSLY BLINDED ADULTS

The techniques and instructional strategies described in the remainder of this book are meant for adventitiously blinded adults (i.e., those who have experienced a significant vision loss) who have as a goal independent travel in familiar and/or unfamiliar urban environments. Emphasis is placed on the need to regain ability and confidence in travel following a significant loss in function. Therefore, the instructor strives to build skill and confidence by creating a history of success. In order to do so, the introduction of skills to be learned, the tasks to be performed and the environments of travel are carefully sequenced and paced.

An Ideal Sequence

Instruction often begins by introducing the student to human guide (also known as sighted guide) procedures. These procedures are the least threatening form of independent travel and require few decisions on the part of the traveler initially. The guide provides the student with protection from obstacles in the environment and bears the responsibility for navigation. The student, then, is free to concentrate on the use of the other senses, interpret the information provided by them and by the guide's movement, and learn the environment in which instruction is taking place.

Self-protective and positional techniques are often taught next. Self-protective techniques provide the traveler the opportunity to move about in space independently and afford some limited protection for the traveler. The upper-hand-and-forearm technique protects the traveler from objects at shoulder and head height, the lower-hand-and-forearm technique provides protection at midline or waist level. Neither technique provides protection from drop-offs (e.g. steps or down-curbs), or is capable of detecting objects in the path of travel much below waist level. Positional techniques for gaining a line of direction from parallel and perpendicular surfaces are often introduced concurrently with self-protective techniques. In this manner the traveler continues to develop orientation skill as he works on travel technique. The introduction of cane skills logically follows self-protective techniques. The diagonal cane technique (the simplest of the cane skills) extends the usefulness of the lower-hand-and-forearm technique by extending the protection from the waist to the floor. However, only one side of the body is protected. As a result, the usefulness of this technique is limited to known, controlled environments. The touch technique is introduced next.

The touch technique is much more complex than the diagonal and provides as complete a protection as experienced by most functionally blind travelers. This technique requires the user to move the cane back and forth protecting both sides equally, while maintaining a collateral movement with the feet to detect drop-offs. A number of variations to the basic cane technique are then introduced.

All techniques mentioned to this point are ideally introduced in controlled indoor environments. Once the touch technique has been mastered, however, other travel environments may be introduced. These environments typically include residential, semi-business, business, and finally all areas of a city via public transit.

The sequence outlined above and followed throughout the remainder of this book assumes a number of ideal conditions. First of all, it assumes that there is a reasonable indoor environment available for use in training. If this is not the case, the instructor will have to introduce most skills and techniques in a residential environment. As a result, the traveller may have little opportunity to develop comfort and skill with straight-line travel (i.e., as is often done using self-protective techniques and the diagonal cane technique in indoor environments) before the touch technique is introduced.

The sequence, as presented, also assumes that there are no demands on the student requiring immediate action. However, this is seldom the case. Persons attending residential programs, for example, are often expected to function on their own within the facility in the evening and on weekends from the day they arrive. Persons attending community centers may have to make their own way in to attend training programs and thus will need some skills to do so. Others recieve services from their own homes. If this is an apartment building, much of the basic sequence may be followed as though the client was residing in a residential training centre. However, if the client lives in a single-family dwelling, the instructor may have to introduce a number of skills just to get the client outside for further training. In these and numerous other cases, the necessity for practical solutions takes precedence over ideal sequencing. Thus, each program of instruction must be designed to meet the needs of the student, even when the abilities of the individuals and the goals of instruction are thought to be the same.

2

Human Guide Techniques

USE OF THE HUMAN GUIDE

There is probably no other mobility system as widely used as the human guide. Human guide procedures use another person as a travel aid with the guide always in the lead. The guide's position ensures safety in the same way as other primary aids or devices. Virtually all non-visual travelers use the human guide at some time, whether they rely upon such a guide as a primary tool, or as a supplement to the cane, dog or electronic travel aids. Newly blinded persons and/or the least skilled of travelers may rely upon the human guide as a means for traveling to and around most environments, while the most skilled and more experienced may use a guide only when convenient or necessary.

A basic tenant in O&M instruction is to introduce the basic skills in a logical sequence. Subskills within each basic skill area are also sequenced to ensure that skills are introduced in isolation so that only one new skill is introduced at a time. Thus each skill and subskill must be task-analyzed to identify its prerequisites. The subskills are then introduced in an order which ensures that all prerequisites are introduced before a skill is taught.

The human guide procedures consist of several subskills, including:

(a) accepting and/or refusing aid,
(b) basic human guide,
(c) changing sides (dynamic and static),
(d) doorways,
(e) narrow spaces,
(f) reversing directions,
(g) seating, and
(h) stairways (Hill & Ponder, 1976).

Of these, three are prerequisites to other skills and therefore need to be introduced in a particular order. They are:

(a) basic human guide, a prerequisite to all of the others,
(b) narrow spaces, a prerequisite to dynamic changing sides, and
(c) dynamic changing sides, a prerequisite to doorways.

The others may be introduced in any order. However, they are generally introduced in such a way that the most complex and anxiety provoking are delayed till last. Thus, the following or a similar sequence is often used:

(a) basic human guide,
(b) narrow spaces,
(c) static changing sides,
(d) dynamic changing sides,
(e) reversing directions,
(f) doorways,
(g) stairways,
(h) seating,
(i) accepting and/or refusing aid.

HUMAN GUIDE: BASIC TECHNIQUE

Objectives

1. To safely and efficiently travel with another person as a guide in a variety of environments.

2. To interpret environmental information through the movement of the guide's body.

3. To develop skills in orientation, sensory awareness and environmental interpretation for later independent travel.

4. To provide a socially acceptable and efficient means of traveling with another person.

Procedure

1. The experienced guide establishes contact by placing her elbow or arm in direct contact with the arm of the traveler. The guide faces in the direction of desired travel and stands slightly in front of the traveler. This position

    (a) avoids excessive maneuvering while initiating travel,
    (b) ensures that the traveler and guide are appropriately aligned, and
    (c) keeps the traveler from being forced to back up when establishing his grip.

2. When contact is not initiated by the guide, the traveler may establish contact by gauging the position of the guide, flexing the arm nearest the guide and moving it toward her until contact is made with the back of the hand. This movement should be done in a manner

   (a) which is slow and natural, while
   (b) ensuring that contact is not made in an inappropriate place.

3. The guide's arm is comfortably grasped just above the elbow with the fingers placed on the inside and the thumb on the outside of the guide's arm. The grip forms a yoke which

   (a) promotes optimal feedback from the guide arm,
   (b) prevents the traveler from continuing forward after the guide has stopped, and
   (c) allows normal arm movement for the guide.

   The grip should be firm enough to assure continuous contact, but should not be uncomfortable for either party.

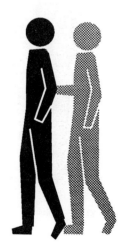

4. The traveler's upper arm is positioned parallel to and near the side of the body in a natural and comfortable position. The arm is held near the side to control the width of the pair and to ensure that the traveler does not swing out from the guide.

Positioning the arm in this manner ensures that the pair occupy the space of about one and a half bodies. This width is fairly easy for the guide to control.

5. The traveler's forearm is flexed at the elbow to approximately 90 degrees and parallel to the floor. This position, along with keeping the arm parallel to the side, ensures that the traveler maintains a constant distance of about one step behind the guide. The distance is determined by the length of the forearm and is therefore constant from guide to guide. This distance provides adequate reaction time for the safety of the traveler. The angle at the elbow may vary slightly depending on the discrepancy in height between the two people.

6. The traveler's shoulder is positioned directly in line with the guide's. This relationship is maintained as long as the traveler keeps the upper arm near the body, in a natural position. The maintenance of constant spatial relationships between the pair promotes a constant relationship between the traveler and his environment. The traveler is always one step behind the guide and is aligned from inside shoulder to inside shoulder. The guide then becomes a reference to objects in the environment.

7. Upon completion of travel, the guide may initiate a break in contact by outwardly rotating the guide arm as a non-verbal cue to disengage. A verbal cue is also appropriate.

The basic human guide procedures work well with the majority of people. However, there are times when the basic technique requires modification.

Modifications to the Basic Technique

Children, or others who are considerably shorter than their guides may establish their grip on the guide's arm anywhere from the guide's wrist on up to the elbow. The exact position is dictated by the need to maintain a 90-degree angle between the upper and lower arm. This position ensures adequate reaction time and tends to be more comfortable than reaching up to the elbow or being pulled by the hand (Hill & Ponder, 1976).

The guide should keep her arm down and to her side while avoiding the temptation to hold the child's hand. The point is to maintain the human guide procedure as an independent or semi-independent mobility system.

Travelers who have difficulty maintaining their balance or otherwise need support when walking may modify the grip, looping their arm around the guide's arm and over the forearm. The guide changes the position of her arm from one that is generally held down along her side to one which forms a 90-degree angle at the elbow. This modification provides a base of support for the transfer of weight. Some reaction time is forfeited by reducing the distance between the guide and the traveler. However, the pace is usually somewhat slower with this modification and therefore the need for rapid response is lessened (LaGrow & Blasch, 1992).

Typically, the guide sets the walking pace. However, an experienced traveler should take responsibility for modifying the pace where needed. Often, an inexperienced guide tends to walk very slowly and deliberately. Such a pace may be quite awkward and often tends to lower the traveler's confidence in the abilities of the guide. A normal cadence is usually more comfortable for everybody and is required to establish a clear kinesthetic understanding of the distances traveled, the length of halls or streets, and the relative distances between numerous environmental features. The quicker walking pace also heightens the awareness of auditory changes. The traveler can increase the pace by applying slight forward pressure on the guide's arm. Conversely, one may slow a guide who is traveling too fast for the conditions of the environment, or simply for comfort, by holding the guide back. A verbal indication is also appropriate.

Teaching Considerations

The instructional pattern, the method for introducing and organizing environmental information and the mode of interaction between student and teacher are introduced along with the basic technique for using a human guide. These procedures will be used throughout the entire O&M sequence. The instructor initially introduces the basic human guide procedure, then begins to familiarize the student with the hallways, cardinal directions (N.S.E.W.) and major landmarks. Instruction begins in wide, uncluttered hallways. The environment is controlled so that there are no spaces narrower than one and a half body widths, there are no doors to be manipulated, and no stairs to ascend or descend. The teacher initiates movement and points out the direction of travel and the names of the hallways traveled. As instruction continues, the student is given increasing responsibility for both maintaining his orientation and making decisions concerning the directions and hallways to travel in order to reach specific objectives.

Standard Teaching Sequence

1. The student is given more responsibility to interpret the guide's

movement. This is done by asking the student the directions traveled and to name and keep track of the hallways of travel.

2. The instructor continues to withdraw information for orientation and shifts the responsibility to the student. At this point, the student may be given a destination and asked how to get there.

3. There is a shift from dependency on the instructor to self-dependency. Up to this point the student usually confirms decisions through the instructor. Commonly, the student would say 'this is where we turn, right?' At this point, the instructor asks the student to confirm, (i.e., 'what do you think?').

4. The student's responsibility for interpreting the guide's movement is again increased. One of the goals of instruction is to prepare the student for dealing with inexperienced or inefficient guides. This means the student has to take responsibility for his own safety when the guide is failing to adequately perform. The instructor then may introduce some imperfection in the guiding system. The student should respond by

   (a)   moving in behind the guide,
   (b)   directing the guide verbally and/or manually, and
   (c)   providing the guide with instructions for improving her technique.

Throughout the entire sequence of human guide instruction, students should be taught the procedures well enough to train their own guides. Most guides are taught by those who use them.

The guide should travel at a reasonably brisk pace. Travelers tend to respond to auditory and kinesthetic input with greater ease when this is done. Auditory perception may also be enhanced by keeping relatively near to the walls during travel. The student must learn to recognize the opening of intersecting hallways, to some extent by hearing the difference in ambient sound reflected off the surface of the wall and the lack of this reflection when the intersecting hall is encountered. The instructor should also initially seek to make crisp and well defined turns, since the recognition of changes in direction is due in part to the vestibular sense. The vestibular system responds to the initiation and cessation of movement. Thus the more defined and clear these are, the more aware the student will be of changes in direction.

The instructor should keep these considerations in mind throughout the entire O&M sequence. The pattern for further instruction is developed right from the start. The move from dependence on the instructor to independence is established in the first lesson. Involvement of the instructor is generally intensive when introducing new skills, techniques and/or environments but decreases as the student gains experience and success and assumes greater responsibility. This occurs over and over again throughout the training sequence (LaGrow, 1990).

NARROW SPACES

Objective

To allow movement through a space which is too narrow to be comfortably or safely negotiated with the basic human guide positioning.

Procedure

1. The guide initiates the technique by moving her guide arm behind and toward the small of her back. The movement of the guide arm provides a non-verbal cue that a narrow space is about to be negotiated. The repositioning of the guide's arm helps to align the traveler directly

behind the guide. They now occupy one, rather than one-and-a-half body widths.

2. The traveler responds by fully extending his arm and stepping in directly behind the guide. The arm is extended to avoid stepping on the heels of the guide.

3. When the narrow space has been negotiated, the guide returns the guide arm to the normal position. The traveler responds similarly.

Teaching Considerations

The guide's movements to initiate and terminate the narrow space procedure may be exaggerated initially to help the student learn to interpret the cues (Hill & Ponder, 1976). When this procedure is first introduced, the guide should glance over her shoulder to be certain the student has assumed the proper position. Narrow spaces are initially introduced in wide, uncluttered hallways where there is no need for the procedure, and no immediate danger if the procedure is executed incorrectly.

When proficiency has been demonstrated, the pair move into environments that are narrower and/or more congested, where the procedure must be used appropriately if the student is to negotiate the space safely. The guide should maintain a consistent frontal alignment when traversing the narrow space to avoid inadvertent false cues. This is important as there appears to be a natural tendency for guides to turn slightly to the side when negotiating narrow spaces.

Modifications to the Basic Technique

Children, or others who are much shorter than their guides, may allow their grip to slide down the guide's forearm toward the wrist when moving into narrow spaces (Hill & Ponder, 1976). This modification increases the distance between the guide and the traveler, helping the traveler avoid stepping on the guide's heels. On the other hand, tall people may need to shorten their stride and/or move their grip up the guide's arm slightly to avoid stepping on the guide.

The narrow space procedure may be modified to use sidestepping when spaces are too narrow to accommodate a single body width, as is the case with aisles of seats in auditoriums or classrooms. Here, the guide would move up to the aisle to be entered, and would begin to move laterally into the aisle. The traveler moves laterally with the guide, maintaining contact with the guide by either extending his arm out fully to the side or by dropping the grip and following forearm to forearm. The traveler moves up next to the guide as the two move laterally. The guide pauses when the traveler is in the aisle and directly behind the first seat. At this point the traveler can contact the back of the seat in front with the back of his free hand. This contact helps the traveler negotiate the space. When leaving the aisle, the guide will usually precede the traveler, but an experienced traveler may simply trail to the aisle and be joined there by the guide.

Anytime the guide initiates the narrow space technique, timing is important. The amount of time the pair are in the narrow space alignment should be kept at a minimum to avoid discomfort and anxiety on the part of the traveler.

Narrow spaces and transferring sides should be introduced before doorways, since both of these techniques include a modified narrow space procedure. This procedure is typically introduced before stairways as well. The stairway technique does not involve narrow spaces, but does require the student to be positioned between the guide and the handrail. This positioning may require the student to change sides before using the stairwell. This may be accomplished prior to reaching the stairwell using the dynamic transferring sides technique which involves a modified narrow spaces procedure. Furthermore, the narrow spaces technique is usually introduced early in the sequence because it does not create as much anxiety as some other procedures, and its use opens up the environment for a greater range of travel and further development of orientation skills.

An experienced traveler may assume the narrow spaces position without signal from the guide to compensate for an inefficient or inexperienced guide, or whenever the environment seems congested and self-protection is required.

TRANSFERRING SIDES

Objective

To enable the traveler to change the position from one side of the guide to the other, either for personal preference or to respond to the dictates of the environment.

Procedure

1. Either party may initiate this technique verbally.

2. If the pair are stationary at the time (static), the traveler

   (a) places the back of his free hand against the back of the guide arm just above the grip,
   (b) releases the grip,
   (c) turns 90 degrees, and
   (d) trails across the guide's back until her opposite arm is contacted. At that point, the traveler re-establishes the grip and turns 90 degrees to assume the basic human guide position on the opposite side of the guide.

3. If the pair are moving at the time (dynamic), the traveler

(a)   contacts the guide arm with the free hand,

(b)   extends his arms fully while stepping in behind the guide,

(c)   changes hands on the guide arm while releasing the initial grip,

(d)   trails this hand across the guide's back to her other arm,

(e)   establishes contact with that arm,

(f)   releases the grip on the original arm,

(g)   continues over to the opposite side of the guide, and

(h)   changes hands on the guide arm while stepping up to assume the basic human guide position.

The procedures as outlined above are designed to maintain continuous contact between the student and the guide, and to utilize the guide as a trailing surface to ensure that the student successfully locates the guide's opposite arm.

Modifications to the Basic Technique

The amount of contact between traveler and guide using the techniques described above is excessive for most people. Anyone with a fairly accurate body sense and kinesthetic awareness can easily move across the guide from side to side without trailing. However, the basic technique described above facilitates success on the initial trials. Most students drop the trailing after a few trials. Those requiring the extra contact may simply continue to use the basic technique without further modification.

The guide may assist the traveler by extending the opposite arm back to meet him, or may also slow the pace somewhat to make the dynamic change of sides smoother (Hill & Ponder, 1976).

The static changing sides technique requires two full body widths to accomplish. However, the technique can be accomplished in the space presently occupied by the pair if the guide moves laterally as the traveler crosses her back. In this fashion, the guide's arm is intercepted sooner and the pair actually change places.

Changing sides is sequenced after narrow spaces as the dynamic technique requires a modified narrow space. However, the static technique could be taught immediately after the basic human guide technique if needed, since there is no other prerequisite skill involved.

Once the student has demonstrated a degree of mastery with basic human guide, narrow spaces and changing sides, the training environment can be expanded by introducing a technique for handling closed doors. Before this is done, however, it may be convenient to introduce the reversing directions technique.

REVERSING DIRECTIONS

Reversing directions is a technique which enables the guide and student to turn 180 degrees without using more space than they currently occupy (Hill & Ponder, 1976). Prior to the introduction of reversing directions, the guide and traveler turn 180 degrees by having the guide walk around the traveler, who acts as a pivot. In this way the traveler is not swung out into space as would be the case if the guide pivoted in place. Making an about-face with the guide as the pivot is not appropriate during the early days of travel. Such a move may result in disorientation for the student and may be unsafe. Pivoting to about-face requires at least two full body widths. This technique is perfectly appropriate as long as space for the movement is available.

Objectives

1. To enable the traveler and guide to complete a 180-degree turn.

2. To make a complete turn in a limited space using no more than the space presently occupied by the pair. This may be an important consideration in an elevator or other crowded and/or restricted space.

3. To enable the guide to control the relationship between the traveler and the environment with a minimum of adjustment. The benefit here is often realized when repeated trials are needed during instruction and the guide wishes to keep the student's position constant relative to some environmental feature (i.e., door or stairway).

Procedure

1. Either the guide or traveler initiates this move by saying 'reverse directions'. This can also be done non-verbally as the guide and student become familiar enough with one another to anticipate each other's movements.

2. The pair stop walking. The traveler releases his grip on the guide's arm. Both then turn toward one another completing a 180-degree turn. This movement looks more natural than turning away from one another.

3. Upon completion of the turn, the guide steps forward and re-establishes contact with the traveler. The traveler may flex the opposite arm to a 90-degree angle while turning to facilitate renewed contact.

Modifications to the Basic Technique

Some persons may become easily disoriented and wish to maintain contact throughout the entire procedure. In this case

(a)   The pair would come to a complete stop.

(b)   They then turn 90 degrees to face one another, while maintaining contact through the guide arm.

(c)   Upon completion of the 90-degree turn the traveler contacts the guide's free arm with his free hand.

(d)   The traveler drops the original grip once the new grip has been established.

(e)   The pair continue the turn to complete the about-face.

The traveler is required to make two 90-degree turns while standing in place. The guide, however, would have to

(a)   step back,

(b)   turn 90 degrees,

(c)   wait for the new grip to be established,

(d)   turn 90 degrees, and

(e)   complete the turn by stepping forward.

This is done to re-establish the guide's position one step in front as the turn is completed. The movement on the part of the guide also ensures that the traveler will not be forced to back up to re-establish the relationship required by the basic human guide procedure.

This modification may also be desirable with persons who have difficulty making accurate 90 and 180-degree turns. This procedure allows for an opportunity to practice turns in a manner which is both functional and practical. The likelihood of practice resulting in more accurate turns is enhanced with this technique, since tactile and kinesthetic feedback is provided with each turn as the student contacts the guide, and positions himself alongside the guide.

This technique does not necessarily need to be introduced at this point in the human guide sequence. In fact, it could be introduced at any point after the basic human guide technique. However, the reversing directions procedure is usually introduced before the doorways and stairway techniques since teaching these skills often includes repeated approaches and trials. Using this technique, the guide may continually go back and forth through a door or up and down stairs, with the student remaining in a constant, relative position to the hinge or railing. If the guide made an about-face pivoting around the student, they would have to change sides after each turn to maintain a constant relative position to the door or stairwell.

CLOSED DOORS

Closed doors can be safely negotiated without the traveler in any way contacting the door. However, that would do nothing to promote the independence of the individual, nor would it add anything to the stature of human guide as a method of independent travel. Finally, it would deny the guide the help and participation of the traveler in the handling of doors. Therefore, a procedure promoting and requiring active participation on the part of the traveler is typically used.

Objectives

1. To enable the traveler to safely and efficiently negotiate closed doors.

2. To provide a method which promotes active participation on the part of the traveler.

Procedure – Doors opening on the traveler's side

1. As the door is reached and manipulated by the guide using her free hand,the traveler steps in and behind the guide. No verbal cue is given or needed with this technique as the traveler can determine what is happening by interpreting the guide's body movements and numerous auditory cues.

   The guide may move her guide arm toward the small of the back, narrowing the space occupied by the pair. The traveler, however, does not need to move completely behind the guide. Most doors are wide enough to accommodate two with slight modification.

2. The traveler moves his free hand out and forward at about waist height in a clearing movement. The elbow is crooked, bringing the upper arm out and forward to protect the body. This height appears to be comfortable and less conspicuous than others. For better leverage the traveler may need to bring his arm up to shoulder height when negotiating heavier doors.

3. The palm is rotated toward the door. The fingers are flexed and relaxed. The arm is moved from midline out until the door is contacted. Contact may be made with either the palm or the side of the hand.

4. The traveler holds the door until it is cleared, releases it, and resumes the normal position.

When the door is opened, the guide moves through and hands the door back to the traveler. With doors opening out, the traveler is required to follow the guide into the doorway about a step and a half before the door is contacted. When the door opens inward, contact may be made as soon as the guide continues forward movement. Practice is often required to build confidence and skill.

Practice is initially provided with the door always opening on the same side. Subsequently, the reversing directions procedure may be used.

Procedure – Doors opening on the opposite side of the traveler

1. As the traveler realizes that the door is opening on the side of the guide, he extends his arm, moves behind the guide and establishes a new grip on the guide arm with his free hand.

2. The original grip is released, and the hand is moved out and forward toward the door. The elbow is crooked bringing the upper arm out and forward to protect the body.

3. The palm is rotated out toward the door until contact is made.

4. The door is held until it is cleared. As the door is released, the traveler steps back to the guide's side and resumes the basic human guide position.

The procedures described here assume that the doors are self-closing. Other doors may be handled by the traveler manipulating the door by its handle and the pair pausing as the door is cleared to allow time to close it.

Teaching Considerations

Practice is typically provided with the door opening on the student's side initially, then with it opening on the opposite side, and finally with it opening on either side. In this fashion, the procedure can be mastered for any location of the door.

Initial instruction usually involves some verbal indication of the location of the door. As proficiency increases, verbal indication is dropped in favor of auditory and kinesthetic interpretation. The student may also begin to anticipate the guide's movement as skill in orientation is expanded. For example, fire doors should push to exit and pull to enter. Therefore, the student may anticipate the direction the door will open before the door is reached.

Modifications to the Basic Technique

The basic technique may have to be modified to include a complete change of sides for children so that they may reach across the guide's girth to handle doors opening on the guide's side.

The technique may also be modified to suit the needs of persons who cannot react quickly enough to handle doors which are simply handed back by the guide, or who are not strong enough to handle doors when they are contacted anywhere but at the very edge, where maximum leverage is possible (LaGrow & Blasch, 1992).

The following technique was developed to meet these needs.

Procedure – Doors opening on the traveler's side

1. As the door is reached, the guide contacts the door with the free hand, pushes or pulls the door as necessary, and transfers the door to the guide hand. The traveler is aware that the door is opening on his side by the transfer of the door from the guide's free hand to the guide hand. This is the only time the guide hand is used to manipulate objects in the environment. Additional auditory and kinesthetic cues confirm the location of the door. The traveler determines if the door is opening in or out by the movement of the guide's body as she moves forward to push or forward and then back to pull. When pushing the door, the guide should wait until the edge of the door is nearly parallel to the frontal plane before transferring it to the guide hand. If this is not done, the guide arm could be pulled away from the student as the transfer is made.

2. The door is held at its edge until the traveler takes it from the guide. This is done to

    (a) take advantage of leverage making the door relatively light and easy to handle,

    (b) keep the traveler's hands away from the hinges, and

    (c) allow the traveler time to react and handle the door without fear that the door will close prematurely.

3. The traveler responds by moving his free hand up to the guide arm and out to take the door from the guide.

4. The guide releases the door and steps through as the traveler follows.

5. The traveler releases the door when it is even with the frontal plane of the body. The traveler can gain extra time to clear the area by giving the door a push as it is released.

Procedure - Doors opening on the guide side

1. As the door is reached, the guide contacts the door with the free hand, pushing or pulling it as necessary. The traveler is aware that the door is opening on the side of the guide by the guide's body movements, auditory cues, and the lack of movement in the guide arm. No transfer of the door from the free hand occurs.

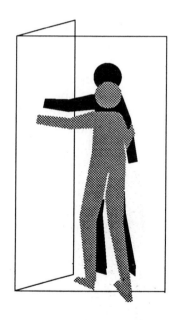

2. The guide holds the door open at its edge until the door is taken from her hand by the traveler.

3. The traveler responds by

   (a)   gripping the guide arm with the free hand,

   (b)   releasing the original grip and using that hand to trail across the back and up the guide's arm to the door, while

(c)   stepping behind the guide to take the door from the guide.

4. The guide releases the door and steps through as the traveler follows.

5. The traveler releases the door when it is positioned parallel, steps back to the side of the guide, and re-establishes the original grip and position.

Some instructors prefer to introduce their students to closed doors in this manner. Students who need the extra information, time and support provided by this modification can continue to use it without experiencing the failure which may precede the introduction of modifications otherwise. Other students may use the extra contact and trailing aspects offered here for only a short time as they progress toward a technique which is very much like the basic procedure described initially. In fact, when done rapidly, the only differences between this and the basic procedure are the use of the guide arm to handle the door, thus the added cue provided by its use, and the commitment on the part of the guide to hold the door open until the student takes it from the guide's hand. Thus the handling of doorways can be streamlined to meet the individual abilities of the user.

Social Graces

For certain travelers, observing social graces between the sexes is important and various modifications are warranted according to the gender of the traveler.

Male traveler with a female guide

1. The guide centers herself directly in front of the door handle. By prior arrangement, the traveler then knows the location of the

door handle and no verbal indication or guidance is necessary.

2. The guide, however, verbally indicates whether the door will be opening to the left or to the right. This could also be accomplished non-verbally by some pre-arranged signal between the pair.

3. The traveler moves around behind the guide in the direction the door will open, contacts the door using the lower arm and forearm, trails the door to its edge and up to find its handle. The traveler may change sides with the guide to facilitate this move.

4. The traveler opens the door and holds it for the female guide. He then follows behind in the normal position.

5. The guide pauses while the traveler closes the door and then resumes travel.

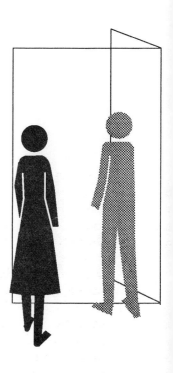

The only real difference between this technique and the basic method for handling closed doors is that the door is opened by the traveler, a function normally carried out by the guide.

Female traveler with male guide

1. The guide approaches the door in such a way that the traveler is centered to the door.

2. The guide disengages his guide arm by outwardly rotating it. The guide then places his hand on the traveler's arm or

back in order to guide her through the opening. This is accomplished by applying gentle pressure with the hand.

3. The guide needs to position himself on the side of the traveler to which the door will open. This may be accomplished before the door is reached, or as the guide arm is moved from being in front of the traveler to her back. If a change of sides is required, the guide would probably not move back to the original side after the door is closed.

4. The guide opens the door, holds it, and guides the traveler through the opening. The guide needs to control the traveler's position and progress as this is done. The traveler should be cautious at this point since the protection normally afforded by the human guide is forfeited.

5. Once through the door, the guide moves up alongside the traveler and reassumes the normal human guide position.

Initially, the modifications described above may seem somewhat awkward. However, with practice and experience the pair can begin to anticipate one another's movements. As a result, these procedures can become quite smooth and graceful.

ASCENDING AND DESCENDING STAIRWAYS

Stairways are often introduced late in the human guide sequence, although basic human guide is the only prerequisite. The reason this is done is to provide the student with numerous opportunities to be successful before traversing stairs. Negotiating stairways while using a human guide probably provokes most anxiety in travelers. This seems to be particularly true for older persons. Anxiety may be minimized if ascending stairs are introduced initially with very short stairways (i.e., 2 to 3 steps), followed by descending stairs, and then progressing to stairways of normal length. Of course, not all teaching environments afford this luxury. The use of handrails, especially at first, may be helpful for some.

Objective

To enable the pair to safely and efficiently ascend and descend stairways.

Procedure

1. The traveler is positioned between the guide and the handrail. The guide approaches the stairs perpendicular to the stairway, stopping or pausing when her toes are at the edge of the first step or riser. This is done to ensure a constant distance (about 1/2 step) between the traveler and the stair/step.

2. The guide pauses at the edge of the first step before beginning the ascent. The combination of the pause and the upward movement of the guide arm act as a nonverbal cue for ascending stairways. The pause, in a sense, prompts the traveler to be ready for a change. The upward movement of the guide arm indicates ascending stairs. Initially, the guide may stop completely before ascent.

3. The traveler shifts his weight forward, detects the first step, steps up and follows, remaining one stair/step behind the guide. The weight is shifted forward to enhance balance and promote safety.

4. The guide pauses slightly and then steps out and forward when the traveler reaches the landing. The combination of the pause and forward movement of the guide arm is a non-verbal cue indicating that the last step has been negotiated. The traveler resumes the normal 90-degree angle from upper arm to lower arm of the basic human guide procedure.

Descending stairs involves a similar process. However, in descending the guide pauses with her toes just at the edge of the first step. The pause and then downward motion of the arm is the non-verbal cue indicating descent. The traveler's response is to shift the center of gravity over the heels and follow the guide down, while remaining one stair/step behind. The guide pauses at the landing and then steps out and forward. This combined cue indicates that there are no more steps to negotiate.

Teaching Considerations

The traveler may wish to slide the foot forward to find the first step. This movement should be a natural continuation of forward motion, and not a probing hesitant exploration of the surface in front. Having located the step with the slide, the opposite foot takes the first step. Taking the step with the forward foot risks catching the heel. Initially, the guide may approach the stairs, pause and provide the student the opportunity to locate the first step repeatedly before stairs are actually ascended or descended. In this fashion, the student may become kinesthetically familiar with the location of the first step. In this case, the guide needs to approach the steps perpendicularly to ensure a consistent distance between the student and the first step. The student may then dispense with the sliding of the foot and simply step out and down or up to the first stair/step.

Modifications to the Basic Technique

The basic stairway technique can be easily adapted by adding verbal cues, using handrails, having the guide provide physical support, and by slowing the pace.

The technique for ascending and descending stairs works well with single steps or curbs (Hill & Ponder, 1976). Irregularities in the environment or design of the stairway may require some verbal intervention. Most situations, however, can be adequately handled with the basic technique by simply interpreting the movements of the guide arm.

SEATING

Often in the course of traveling the need arises to locate a seat and be seated. Potentially, seating can be awkward and embarrassing for both the guide and the traveler. Procedures have been developed for seating with chairs, at tables and in auditoriums or bleachers. These techniques are readily adaptable to a variety of seating situations.

Objective

To enable the pair to efficiently handle a variety of seating situations with grace and ease.

Procedure

Chair:

This procedure may be employed with any

kind of chair which does not have to be pulled out for use.

1. The guide approaches the chair and positions the traveler in close proximity to the seat. When possible, the traveler may be positioned so that he is in physical contact with the chair. This is done to minimize the amount of verbal information needed.

2. If contact is not made, the guide informs the traveler of the relative position of the chair.

3. The traveler contacts the chair with the front of the lower leg.

4. If contact is made with the back or the side of the chair, the traveler maintains contact with the chair and moves around to the front.

5. The traveler examines the chair by moving his hand down the back and across the seat. This is done to determine the type of chair it is, to ensure that there is a back, and to be sure that the chair is clear of objects. This step may be eliminated when traveling with a reliable guide.

6. The traveler turns and places the back of his legs against the front edge of the chair and is seated, adjusting the chair for stability.

Seating at a table:

1. The traveler is guided to the back of the chair.

2. The traveler locates the back of the chair with the lower hand and forearm, then moves his hand over the back of the chair and forward until the table is contacted.

3. The traveler places one hand on the edge of the table and one hand on the back of the chair.

4. The traveler pulls the chair out while maintaining contact with the table.

5. The traveler steps in between the table and chair, sits down and pulls the chair back up to a comfortable position.

6. When rising, the traveler contacts the table, stands and pushes the chair back to provide enough room to maneuver.

7. The traveler then pushes the chair back into place at the table, breaks contact with both the table and chair, and re-establishes contact with the guide. Contact is maintained between the chair and table to provide the traveler with a kinesthetic reference for placement and movement of the chair.

Auditorium seating:

The procedure described here may be used for seating in an auditorium, stadium, on bleachers or with rows of desks. This procedure includes a modified narrow-space technique. As such, it must be sequenced after narrow spaces. The rest of the seating procedures have no prerequisites other than basic human guide, and therefore, can be introduced anywhere in the teaching sequence.

1. The pair proceed down the aisle to the selected row with the guide positioned between the traveler and the side of the row to be entered.

2. The guide begins to sidestep into the aisle. The traveler moves up and alongside the guide as they move laterally into the aisle.

3. The guide pauses when the traveler has entered the aisle and is positioned directly behind the first seat. The traveler moves the free hand forward and contacts the back of the seat with the back of the hand.

4. The traveler follows the guide laterally while maintaining contact with the seats in front of the pair. This is done to avoid contact with the feet and knees of people already seated as the pair move toward their seats. The student should be warned not to let his hand stray over the backrest in order to avoid inadvertent contact with others.

5. When the seats are reached, the guide

pauses while positioning the traveler directly in front of the intended seat. They are then seated.

6. To exit, the guide may have to step around in front of the traveler before establishing contact.

Sidestepping may not be necessary if there are no others seated between the pair and the desired seat or aisle.

Social Graces

Slight adaptations to these techniques are required when the guide and traveler are different sexes and they wish to be socially correct in their handling of various seating arrangements.

Male guide with a female traveler

The guide leads the traveler to the chair and holds it while she is being seated. If the chair is at a table, he

    (a)   leads the traveler to her chair,
    (b)   pulls it out,
    (c)   holds it for her as she is being seated, and
    (d)   re-positions it to the table before going to his chair.

When leaving the table, the guide

    (a)   goes to the traveler's place at the table,
    (b)   pulls her chair back,
    (c)   holds it as she rises, and

(d)   moves the chair back into position at the table before re-establishing the basic human guide procedure for further travel

Female guide with a male traveler

A female guide needs to make a few more adaptations to the basic technique if the male is to be provided the opportunity to be socially correct.

The guide leads the traveler to the chair, bringing him into contact with the back of it. If the pair are to be seated at a table, the traveler should be positioned between the guide's seat and his own. The guide leaves him in contact with both the chair and the table. In this way, the traveler can pull the chair out and hold it for the female guide, while remaining kinesthetically aware of its relative position to the table allowing for a smooth and accurate replacement.

The guide disengages from the traveler and moves around and in front of the traveler to be seated. The male continues to hold the chair until the guide is seated. He may then move laterally, with or without contact with the table to his chair, pull it out and be seated. When leaving, the male

(a)   gets up,
(b)   contacts the table and the back of the chair,
(c)   pushes his chair back into position at the table,
(d)   moves laterally to the guide's chair,
(e)   contacts the chair and table,

(f)   pulls the chair back and holds it
         while the guide gets up, and moves
         over to stand beside the chair away
         from the guide.

The traveler then pushes the chair back into
position at the table, breaks contact with both
the table and chair while stepping back to
wait for the guide. The guide then comes back
to the traveler to re-establish the basic human
guide procedure.

Instruction in human guide techniques does not allow for much
interaction between the traveler and the sighted public. As the
traveler acquires other more independent means of travel,
interaction will increase. Not all interaction, however, will be
desired or, if desired, appropriate. As a result, travelers must
learn to deal with the public and their offers of assistance.

ACCEPTING OR REFUSING ASSISTANCE

Sighted persons are often willing to help a blind traveler. However,
few actually know how to perform as a human guide. As a result,
the traveler must be ready to take charge to ensure that the
assistance offered, if accepted, is appropriate. Of course, the
traveler may also wish to simply refuse the aid. A procedure,
known as the Hine's Break, provides the traveler with a means
of accepting or refusing aid when physical contact is involved in
the offer (Hill & Ponder, 1976).

Objectives

1. To enable the traveler to gain control of a
   situation involving physical contact with a
   helping person.

2. To provide the traveler with a means of

graciously accepting or refusing assistance when it is offered.

3. To provide the traveler with a means of immediately establishing appropriate relationships between himself and an inexperienced guide.

Procedure

1. When an offer of assistance is accompanied by physical contact, the traveler responds by relaxing the grasped arm and pulling it across his body toward his opposite shoulder, while planting the feet and shifting the center of gravity back. The arm is pulled across the body as a means of breaking contact with the would-be guide. The traveler shifts his weight back to keep from being propelled forward and/or turned. The feet are planted firmly to avert the possibility of an inadvertent change of alignment or disorientation while refusing assistance.

2. Once contact has been broken, the individual can verbally indicate the desire to accept or refuse assistance. If assistance is desired, the traveler can grasp the guide's arm and establish the appropriate relationship for basic human guide. If the traveler is holding a cane at the time the arm is grasped, the traveler simply transfers the cane to the free hand before accepting aid.

COMMON COURTESIES AND OTHER CONSIDERATIONS

In addition to the instructional concerns presented thus far, there are also a number of basic courtesies which should be maintained by the guide to ensure the development of rapport and the maintenance of trust with the traveler. First, when entering the room or area occupied by an individual who is blind, it is appropriate for the guide to speak, to alert that person to her presence and to establish her identity. Failure to do this could inadvertently jeopardize the trust between a student and teacher. The student may feel that his privacy is being invaded if the teacher has been in the room unbeknown to him. The same could be true of the relationship between a guide and a traveler. Second, it is inappropriate to leave the traveler standing in the middle of a hallway, room or other open space. The guide should bring the traveler into contact with an object, even if the traveler is only being left momentarily. Finally, the guide should not walk away from the traveler without indicating her intent to do so. The person who is blind may be left in the embarrassing position of carrying on a conversation without an audience.

A mobility instructor should be a model guide, precise in movements and obviously attentive to the environment. As the student gains skill, the guide's movements may become less precise allowing the student the opportunity to take control and exercise independence as a part of the unit. The instructor should provide enough experience and adequate opportunity for practice to ensure that the skills required for using a human guide as a travel aid are ingrained. The instruction should be thorough enough to ensure that the student can train an inexperienced guide as the need arises.

3

Self-Protective and Positional Techniques

There are times when the traveler has a need to move short distances in a familiar controlled environment without the protection of a human guide, cane, guide dog, or electronic travel aid. The self-protective techniques provide a limited amount of protection. However, these techniques are generally adequate for movement in controlled, familiar environments (Hill & Ponder, 1976). Familiar environments are necessary because drop-offs (changes in level) and other obstacles at foot level are not detectable. Protection is afforded from objects located in the traveler's vertical plane a little below the waist and at or around head height. The self-protective techniques may be used to locate specific objects which have a known location, or be used with other primary mobility aids when protection for the head or upper body is required. This is often the case when traveling in non-standard environments.

Exactly when these techniques are introduced into the teaching sequence is somewhat arbitrary, however early introduction is the general rule. Self-protective techniques are generally taught with or precede the positional techniques, which are logical prerequisites to cane skills. The self-protective techniques are at times taught before human guide and are usually taught before the diagonal cane technique. At times, the diagonal is taught before human guide. Decisions of this type are made according to the needs of the student and the dictates of the environment. In any case, the positional and protective techniques should be introduced fairly early in the sequence, since they enhance accuracy in independent movement and promote straight-line travel.

Positional techniques provide the traveler with an opportunity to use existing spatial relationships to establish and maintain a line of travel. Positional techniques include:

(a)   trailing,
(b)   direction-taking (establishing a line of travel from a parallel surface), and
(c)   squaring off (establishing a line of travel from a perpendicular surface).

Historically, these techniques have been collectively referred to as pre-cane skills. However, this term is a misnomer since the various techniques involved, particularly the positional techniques, continue to have application throughout the entire sequence. In fact, these procedures continue to become more varied and complex as the traveler gains skill and experience (Pogrund & Rosen, 1989).

SELF-PROTECTIVE TECHNIQUES

Upper-Hand-and-Forearm

Objectives

1. To protect the upper body generally, and the head and shoulders specifically

    (a)   when traveling short distances in a familiar, controlled environment,
    (b)   when moving about in an unexplored space, and/or

(c)   when used in conjunction with other primary mobility aids while traveling in non-standard or uncontrolled environments.

2. To facilitate the locating of overhanging objects and objects rising from the floor in the vertical plane.

Procedure

1. The arm is flexed to shoulder height and held parallel to the floor. The arm can be raised to provide more direct protection of the face and/or head or lowered to a more comfortable, less conspicuous position when locating objects in the vertical plane such as a door post.

2. The fingers are extended and placed in line with the opposite shoulder, the hand and arm are drawn forward until an obtuse angle (about 120 degrees) with the upper arm is formed at the elbow. The arm is placed forward to provide as much forward protection, hence reaction time, as possible. The hand and forearm should not be extended so far forward as to sacrifice complete coverage from shoulder to shoulder, however.

3. The forearm is inwardly rotated until the palm faces forward. This is done so that the palm of the hand contacts objects first. In this fashion, most of the shock of contact can be absorbed in the hand and wrist.

The arm opposite the point of expected contact is used. This is done to reduce the number of contacts made with the elbow or forearm as compared to those made with the open hand. Common errors by beginning students include: allowing the hand to drift toward midline – reducing lateral coverage; allowing the forearm to come back toward the body – reducing reaction time; and/or turning the body toward the opposite shoulder when extending coverage and thus altering alignment.

The upper-hand-and-forearm technique should be used selectively as protection from known obstacles or to locate specific objects in their environment. Therefore, it is used almost exclusively in familiar environments and usually for a very brief period of time. The exception to this rule is when it is used for familiarization with a room, or when it is used to add head height protection to a primary mobility aid in areas where one suspects there may be a need. The upper-hand-and-forearm technique may most often be used to protect the traveler when passing through open doorways without a cane, or when crossing a grassy parkway (verge) with a cane. In the former situation, the traveler brings the arm up just before reaching the door, contacts the door with the forearm, moves through the door and past the center post, drops the upper-hand-and-forearm and continues on his way. In the latter, the traveler crosses the street, finds that he has veered inside away from the sidewalk (footpath), decides to simply step up over the grass strip and locate the sidewalk perpendicular to his path of travel. Just as the traveler begins to step up into this uncontrolled space (i.e., an area not intended for pedestrian travel) the upper-hand-and-forearm is brought up to protect the upper body from tree limbs and/or guide wires and remains there until the sidewalk is located, usually after three or four steps. These short-term situational applications typify the intended use of the upper-hand-and-forearm technique.

This technique is rather conspicuous and some students object to it. The instructor should be aware of this, and plan its introduction in a way which is the least objectionable for the student.

Lower-Hand-and-Forearm

Objectives

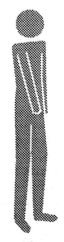

1. To enable the traveler to locate and protect himself from objects at or around waist level while traveling in a familiar, controlled environment.

2. To be used in conjunction with the upper-hand-and-forearm technique to provide protection from the waist to the head while traversing open areas.

Procedure

1. The arm is slightly flexed at the shoulder until the hand is 15 to 20 cm in front of the body.

2. The forearm is held across the body so that the hand is positioned at midline.

3. The fingers are extended and relaxed, with the palm of the hand toward the body.

The lower-hand-and-forearm technique affords protection to the center of the body at and slightly below waist level. This technique may be used to find or protect oneself from desks, tables, chairs or other objects at that height. This technique is often less than satisfactory for tall people, since the hand passes over rather than contacts the objects of concern. A rolled newspaper or magazine may be held to extend the coverage.

At times the lower-hand-and-forearm may work well with the upper-hand-and-forearm. This is usually the case when limited travel within a room or around a building is desired. Typically, if this much protection is needed, cane techniques are preferable.

POSITIONAL TECHNIQUES

Positional techniques are basic to independent travel. The techniques are simple, yet they are used in increasingly complex situations. The traveler establishes his position in space relative to, or by means of

(a)   dominant environmental clues,
(b)   geometric patterns, and
(c)   compass directions.

In all cases, the confidence with which one establishes this position must depend upon the actualization of orientation through movement (Pereira, 1990). In other words, the traveler establishes a hypothesis concerning his position in relation to an object in the environment, then tests the validity of the hypothesis by traveling to the object. A return trip is required to establish that the object found at the end of travel was indeed in line with the mental projection of the traveler. The degree of confidence the person has in orientation should be directly related to the accuracy with which his mental projection has been verified.

Repeated experience with this process should result in increased accuracy and confidence on the part of the traveler in establishing his position in space. However, this would be the case only if the traveler was accurate in his movements, so that a projection from self to an object was indeed verified through travel and reinforced by a return. Accuracy in movement is dependent upon traveling a straight line. Before this can be accomplished, one must first establish a line from which to travel. This line may be established through either parallel or perpendicular alignment.

Parallel Alignment – Trailing

Objectives

1. To facilitate straight-line travel.

2. To enable the traveler to locate specific objectives along an environmental line.

3. To provide the traveler with a means of determining his relative position in space through continuous contact with the environment.

Procedure (trailing a wall by hand)

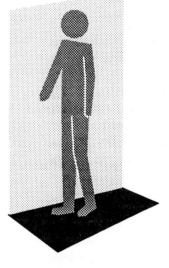

1. The traveler faces the desired direction of travel and is positioned parallel to and near the surface to be trailed.

2. The arm nearest the wall is flexed at the shoulder until the hand contacting the wall is about waist height. In this way, the hand is projected forward providing some reaction time and positioned at about the height of handrails and doorknobs.

3. The hand is pronated and the palm cupped with the fingers slightly flexed and relaxed. This is done to allow the fingers to absorb the shock of contact with objects along the wall, while avoiding the possibility of jamming fingers or having doors close on them.

4. Contact with the trailing surface is

maintained with the ring and little finger.
A person wearing a ring may wish to rotate
it so that it is held in the palm of the hand
for safety.

5. The traveler proceeds along the wall
maintaining light contact with the surface,
while mentally projecting a line parallel to
the trailing surface.

Consistent contact should be maintained with the surface
while trailing. When recessed doors are encountered, however,
the traveler should project a straight line, bring the trailing
hand over to assume a lower-hand-and-forearm position and
cross the opening. After two or three steps, the traveler should
turn slightly into the wall to re-establish contact. At this time
he may wish to initiate the upper-hand-and-forearm technique
with the free hand.

Trailing a wall with the hand is just the first of several trailing
techniques to be utilized to establish a parallel line, find specific
objectives, and/or establish a relative position in space.

Trailing is used throughout independent travel, and various
trailing techniques are introduced throughout the teaching
sequence. Blind and visually impaired persons may employ these
techniques

(a)   tactually as described here, or
(b)   with a long cane,
(c)   visually, if sufficient vision exists and when the occasion
        presents itself,
(d)   auditorially (i.e., trailing parallel traffic),
(e)   while utilizing electronic travel aids, and/or
(f)   in conjunction with the use of a guide dog.

Trailing is best thought of as a selective technique utilized to
meet one of its three stated objectives. Less skilled travelers tend

to rely on trailing more frequently and for greater distances than do more efficient travelers.

Trailing is somewhat inefficient as it puts the traveler in fairly constant contact with objects which are not directly in the path of travel. When trailing in congested areas, it is good practice to conform with the flow of pedestrian traffic to avoid unnecessary contact with others.

Parallel Alignment – Direction-Taking

Objective

To enable the traveler to obtain a general line of direction through the use of parallel surfaces or auditory cues.

Procedure

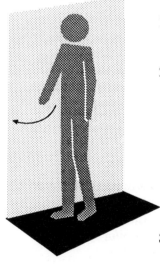

1. The traveler positions the body parallel to the object or sound to be used.

2. When using an object, the traveler uses an arm or leg to tactually establish a parallel alignment. When using parallel auditory cues, the individual projects a line parallel to the line of sound. The traveler should listen until the traffic (i.e., typical sound source) disappears. The further one can follow the sound, the more likely an accurate alignment can be established.

3. The traveler then mentally projects a straight line from the surface or sound trailed to establish a straight line to be traveled.

Perpendicular Alignment – Squaring Off

Objective

To enable the traveler to obtain a general line of direction through the use of a straight line which is perpendicular to the intended line of travel.

Procedure

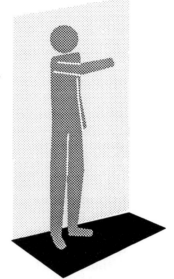

1. The individual systematically positions two or more body parts against the straight surface of an object perpendicular to the line of intended travel.

2. The traveler then mentally projects a straight line of travel into space.

This procedure assumes that the person has aligned the body to conform to the perpendicular surface used for projection. Students are often more successful initially when using doors or walls, where the whole body can be put against the surface, than when using curbs or perpendicular traffic sounds. In the case of the latter, the student should establish alignment with one body part then systematically align the rest of the body before attempting to project from the frontal plane. For example, if alignment is established in relation to perpendicular traffic sounds, the student

    (a)   moves the head in order to establish the point where the sound seems to transfer from one ear to the other, or as they say, when it appears that one's nose is pointing at the traffic as it passes directly in front of the traveler,

    (b)   the shoulders are then aligned to the head,

    (c)   the hips are aligned to shoulders,

(d)   the knees are aligned to the hips, and

(e)   the feet are aligned to the knees.

The positional techniques described above are used in a variety of environments and throughout the entire mobility sequence. They have a major role both in street crossing and familiarization procedures. The perpendicular method is typically used when movement is initiated. A line may be taken from any object perpendicular to the desired line of travel, including the traveler's own frontal plane. This is often done at intersections after an entire block has been successfully negotiated. The traveler stops at the intersection, listens for traffic, determines when it is safe to cross, projects a straight line and continues on his way. This may also follow a facing movement. In this case the traveler stops, turns 90 degrees, projects a straight line and proceeds.

Parallel alignment, on the other hand, is used more often during travel, and tends to be a continuation of forward movement. Although the traveler may stop and listen to traffic or pedestrian sounds, determine direction and then align parallel to it, it is more likely that this is done continuously as one moves through an environment. This may also be done tactually. For example, travelers often contact the grass line with the cane when traveling along sidewalks. The traveler would not correct or move away from the grass line every time it is contacted. Rather, the traveler would try to maintain contact with that grass line for two or three swings of the cane to the side of contact. When this is accomplished, the cane traveler could assume that he is traveling parallel to the surface. Once a parallel line has been established, the traveler could step away enough to break contact with it, project that line and continue on to the immediate objective.

Straight-line travel enhances safety and assists the traveler in avoiding unnecessary contact with peripheral objects. Proper alignment procedures also facilitate systematic search patterns and the establishment of object-to-object relationships. Straight-line travel requires that the traveler

(a)   establish a straight line – usually using techniques for either parallel or perpendicular alignment,
(b)   mentally project a straight line,
(c)   shift his center of gravity forward,
(d)   take a dominant first step, and
(e)   move out maintaining a consistent, and somewhat rapid, pace (Hill & Ponder, 1976).

4

Systematic Search Patterns and Familiarization Procedures

For those who are blind or visually impaired, efficiency in searching an area for dropped or previously placed objects, or becoming familiar with machines, rooms, floors, buildings and outdoor environments is greatly enhanced when a systematic approach is utilized. This observation holds true for tactual or electronic searches, and the travel patterns used to explore larger physical areas, as well as aided or unaided visual searches conducted by low-vision persons. In all cases, the problem is the same. Only a small area can be effectively explored at one time. Therefore, a system is needed to ensure that the entire area to be searched will be covered eventually. Thus, the advent of systematic search patterns.

Typically, this important practical skill is introduced to the student by teaching a method for locating dropped objects and then applying it more generally in the process of becoming familiar with phones, vending machines and small rooms. These procedures underlie more formal methods of investigation collectively known as familiarization techniques.

Techniques for familiarization and for self-familiarization are incorporated throughout the instructional sequence. General concepts underlying the specific techniques are continuously employed as the instructor plans lessons designed to introduce techniques of travel while introducing or expanding the travel environment.

SYSTEMATIC SEARCH PATTERNS

Systematic search patterns may be used to ensure that a surface is thoroughly and completely explored. There are numerous patterns which have been and can be devised to do this. Three of these will be delineated here to illustrate this point. These patterns have a number of general characteristics in common: they

(a)   expand from a starting point as the search progresses,
(b)   rely upon some orientation marker, and
(c)   employ a plan for moving to new areas when the maximum range of search has been reached.

Linear

The linear pattern seeks to systematically cover an area by moving one hand laterally while using the other to mark the spot of origin. The marker hand is placed at the leading edge of the area to be searched. The search hand is placed next to the marker and then moved laterally to the full extent of the individual's reach, or to the edge of the area to be searched, and then it is brought back to the marker. At the end of the sweep (i.e., lateral movement out and back), the marker is moved up to the fingertips of the hand doing the search. That hand is then moved so that it is parallel to the marker hand in order to begin another lateral sweep. This process is repeated until the entire surface is covered.

If the surface is too wide to cover with a single sweep to the side, it may be bisected by moving the marker hand up the center. After half of the surface is thoroughly searched, the marker is drawn back toward the student and it becomes the search hand while the other is used to mark. The remaining half of the surface may be explored as before.

Fan

The fan employs a side-to-side arc which grows ever larger with each sweep of the hand. The search begins at the leading edge of the area to be covered and just to the side of the searcher's midline. The hand used in the search is moved in an arc from side to side. The arc expands with each sweep. This is done until the individual can no longer reach to cover new area.

The search may continue up or to the side depending on the object of the search. If the search is to continue upward, the hand is stopped at the top of the arc, the other hand is used to mark that spot. The person moves up so that the marker hand is in front and just off midline. The marker is replaced with the search hand as the search is continued. If the search is to continue laterally, the search is stopped at the point where the hand is fully extended in the direction of the intended move. The other hand is placed there as a marker while the individual moves laterally so that the marker hand is just off midline. The search then continues with the other hand as done previously.

Expanding Box

The marker hand is placed at the edge of the area to be searched and just below its leading edge. The other hand is brought to it, and is moved

    (a)   laterally,
    (b)   down to the leading edge, and then
    (c)   back and up to the marker forming a box.

The box expands up and to one side with each ensuing sweep. The other sides are defined by the leading edge of the area to be explored and the marker hand. They do not expand.

At the completion of each sweep, the marker and the hand employed in searching are moved up to expand the box. As the search continues, the box is enlarged until the surface is completely covered, or the searcher can no longer reach new areas comfortably.

If the box must be moved up, the marker hand is held in place until the individual moves up to it, gets comfortable, and continues the search. If the search is to continue to the side, the hand used to sweep the area is stopped at the point where it is farthest from the marker. The individual then

(a)　picks up the marker hand,

(b)　moves laterally,

(c)　gets comfortable,

(d)　places the marker hand just above the hand currently marking the new starting point,

(e)　moves the hand up to the marker, and

(f)　begins to describe the new box.

LOCATING DROPPED OR PREVIOUSLY PLACED OBJECTS

Objectives

1. To safely and efficiently locate objects which have been dropped or previously placed.

2. To aid in the development of concepts utilized for systematic exploration.

Procedure

1. With dropped objects, the individual notes the sound of the object as it is dropped, and turns to face the object. With previously placed objects, the person faces its expected location.

2. The individual walks to the object's expected location, slightly underestimating

the distance. This is done to ensure that the object is located within the area of search as each of the search patterns expands outward as the search continues.

3. The individual positions himself for the search. If the object was dropped on the floor, the searcher should squat straight down and protect the head when leaning forward to begin the search. Kneeling without bending at the waist is preferable so that the head is not vulnerable. Persons who need to bend forward to achieve the search position, should employ the upper-hand-and-forearm for protection.

4. A systematic search pattern is used to locate the object. Larger objects may be located by sweeping the area with the long cane if the environment so allows.

The instructor may introduce this skill by dropping an object on a table top. This is done to control the size of the area to be searched, while isolating this skill from the self-protective skills needed for searching uncontrolled areas. Initially, objects may be dropped in front of and fairly close to the student. Searches may be made more difficult by the instructor as the student demonstrates success in finding objects and employing systematic search patterns.

FAMILIARIZATION PROCEDURES

There are two basic types of familiarization procedures used in orientation and mobility. These are other (instructor)-directed familiarization, and self-familiarization.

Other-Directed Familiarization

The traveler can be made familiar with an environment by someone else. In this case, there are two basic procedures which can be followed – familiarization by objective, and directed familiarization.

Familiarization by Objective

Mobility instructors typically use objectives (i.e. destinations for travel) within lessons to provide their students with opportunities to practise the skills taught. In addition, objectives of travel may be used to familiarize the student with the environment of travel. Therefore, the intersections which delineate the boundary of the travel environment, either hallways or streets, are typically used as objectives when new environments are being introduced. Later, other corner objectives are used, and then finally, mid-block objectives are introduced. In this way the traveler

(a)   is given the opportunity to travel the entire length and width of an environment to establish the relative size and shape of the environment,

(b)   learns the names of the streets or hallways which constitute the boundaries of the environment, and gains information about them,

(c)   can be systematically exposed to landmarks and clues which exist in the environment, and

(d)   is gradually introduced to the major features (e.g., busy intersections, parks, schools, bus stops, civic or office buildings, stores and shops) of the environment by traveling to them as objectives for lessons or runs within lessons.

This procedure is continually repeated as students are introduced to floors in buildings, whole buildings, residential environments, semi-business environments, business environments, and department stores, malls and plazas.

Directed Familiarization

Directed familiarization is conducted specifically to familiarize a person with an area. This procedure is often used to provide an initial familiarization with a building or business area. The traveler will develop a more thorough understanding of the area as it is used. The person conducting this procedure typically

(a) walks the traveler through the area to establish the relative size and shape of the environment,

(b) names and provides information concerning the streets or hallways which constitute the borders of the area,

(c) identifies any landmarks which may exist in the area, and

(d) identifies and names the rooms or stores which exist in the area while having the traveler identify the ones that may be of interest.

The instructor then continues the familiarization process by

(a) introducing the traveler to the specific objectives of interest,

(b) identifying landmarks and/or clues which could be used to identify them, and

(c) providing feedback to the traveler as he repeatedly locates the objectives of interest to commit their placement to memory.

This procedure is typically done with one side of a street or hall at a time. Repeated locating of objectives is used to confirm the individual's knowledge of the environment.

Self-Familiarization

Self-familiarization procedures are designed to allow the individual to familiarize himself with objects, rooms and various travel environments. In some cases this may be done without assistance, in others a sighted respondent may be needed as a source of information although not relied upon for the structure or direction of the familiarization process. Almost any sighted person available could be used to assist the traveler, the responsibility for the process rests with the traveler, however.

Familiarization with Phones and Vending Machines

The process used to approach an object such as a phone or vending machine is basically dependent upon its function. The vending machine, for example, can be broken down into four areas of interest. These include:

(a)   buttons for selection,
(b)   pay slot and coin return button,
(c)   slot for change or returned coins, and
(d)   area for dispensing the product.

The buttons for selecting items are usually directly above the area for dispensing the product, as the pay slot is to the area for change and returned coins. The area dealing with the money is typically to the side of the area devoted to the product. Therefore, the machine can usually be explored by locating the product area and the money area, and then establishing the relative position of each.

Once the layout of the machine is known, the person who is visually impaired can acquire sighted assistance to identify the location of the products and their corresponding keys. In some cases this may be needed only once. For example, the product locations in cigarette machines, coffee machines, and soft-drink dispensers are seldom changed and the user's choice of the product dispensed is fairly constant. Therefore, the individual need only memorize the location of one or two buttons in order to use this type of machine on subsequent occasions. Candy, snack and sandwich machines pose a different problem since the product position may change much more often and sighted assistance may be needed when making the selection. However, no help would be needed to use the machine itself (i.e., put in the money, retrieve the product and the change).

Phones are set up in a similar manner. The money slot is directly above the coin return slot, the phone and cradle are directly above the dial or push button, and to one side of the money area. The student may become familiar with different pay phones by

(a)   locating the phone and cradle,
(b)   locating the card or coin slot, return button and slot for returned coins,
(c)   lifting the phone from its cradle and locating the dial or push button panel, and then
(d)   establishing the relative location of each.

Familiarization with Rooms

Rooms may be explored in a number of ways depending on their size, shape and function. The perimeter of the room is explored initially. In some cases a perimeter search may be all that's necessary. This is usually the case with a narrow, rectangular room which has its furnishings located along the walls. However, most rooms require further exploration. This may be done by either utilizing a grid pattern to explore the center of the room, or by establishing a reference point, and locating all objects in relation to it. The purpose of each of these methods is to provide the traveler with a systematic method of self-familiarization, which results in the establishment of workable concepts concerning the function and placement of objects within a given room.

Perimeter

The perimeter of the room is explored initially. The traveler determines

(a)   the size and shape of the room,
(b)   the presence and sequential order of objects found around the perimeter,
(c)   relative position of the objects, and
(d)   whether other methods of exploration are needed.

When utilizing the perimeter method, appropriate protective techniques should be utilized as:

1. The individual establishes a reference point which functions as a marker to identify the beginning and end of each trip around the perimeter. This object needs to be located along the perimeter, should be centrally located and must be fixed and permanent. The door to a room often serves this function best.

2. The size and shape of the environment is determined by trailing the perimeter from start to finish. This movement defines the exterior of the area and aids in the development of a whole concept.

3. Subsequent trips around the perimeter are made to firmly establish the size and shape of the room, identify dominant objects along the trailing surface, and determine the relative position of objects and their placement along specific walls.

4. The traveler further establishes relationships by moving from the reference point to a given object and from object to object. When sighted assistance is available, this may be done by pointing to various objects as the traveler moves about the room. Feedback concerning the accuracy of the response is provided by the sighted person.

5. The individual determines if further exploration is needed and determines to pursue this using either a gridline or reference point.

Grid-line

The grid-line method is used to

(a) establish or verify the relationship of objects located on opposite walls, and
(b) explore the center of a room.

1. After conducting a perimeter search, the traveler is positioned against one wall and one to two meters from another. The individual crosses the room, exploring its center and returns to the starting point. The room is always crossed and then recrossed to confirm that the initial crossing was straight and that any object contacted on the far side was indeed directly across from the starting point.

2. The traveler moves down another one to two meters from the parallel wall and crosses again. This procedure is repeated until the entire room has been crossed in one direction (i.e., east-west).

3. The individual then

(a) moves to the parallel wall and down one to two meters,
(b) turns his back to the wall, and
(c) repeats the procedure until the entire room has been crossed in the remaining direction (i.e., north-south).

The grid-line method allows the traveler to systematically explore the interior of the room. This method is especially useful in rooms where the furnishings are not arranged along the perimeter, or in a predictable pattern.

The method of exploration can be varied. Travelers may wish to dissect the room more by function than by area. If this is the case, the person determines some probable cross-room relationships, and crosses the room to confirm them. Often, a combination of area and function is used to establish the appropriate crossing points.

Reference point

Often when conducting a perimeter search, a particular feature of a room or a piece of furniture proves to be so dominant in the arrangement of the room that it is obvious that there is no reason to continue exploring the room in this fashion. A good example of this may be found in the layout of bedrooms. The bed so dominates the room in many cases that a perimeter technique is difficult to carry out and a grid-line would be ludicrous. In this case, attention should be shifted to the bed.

The positions of other objects in the room are established relative to the bed (i.e., the dresser is on the left side of the the foot of the bed, the phone and alarm clock are on a table left of the head of the bed, the closet is right across from the foot of the bed, and the door is right of the head of the bed on the north wall). The traveler would systematically explore the room in relation to the reference point, and object-to-object relationships would also be developed allowing for a functional understanding of the room.

Structured Solicitation

The traveler can become familiar with buildings and outdoor environments through structured solicitation. Typically this is done by finding one or two objectives as needed, and then building an expanded understanding of the area over time. The purpose of a structured solicitation procedure is to pinpoint the location of a specific objective relative to the nearest intersection (LaGrow & LaDuke, 1990).

The success of this procedure is dependent upon the quality of the answers received, which is in turn dependent upon the quality of the questions posed and the characteristics of the individual from whom the information is gained. The person called upon should be knowledgeable and committed to helping the traveler. A telephone call to the destination itself is often the best way to ensure success.

Rooms Located within Buildings

The traveler must first establish the general layout of a building. This is usually done relative to the building's numbering system. Hallways may be numbered continuously from a given starting point in a linear, clockwise or counter-clockwise fashion. It is important to identify the starting point and the direction of travel (Hill & Ponder, 1976).

Numbers may also be assigned in relation to numbered hallways. The system for assigning numbers to hallways must then be determined. Hallways may be numbered relative to

(a)   the direction of travel,

(b)   their relative position from the building's focal point, and

(c)   the floor on which they are located.

For example, odd-numbered hallways (i.e., 1100, 1300, 1500) may run in one direction (e.g., north-south), and even-numbered ones (i.e., 1200, 1400 and 1600) in the other (e.g., east-west).

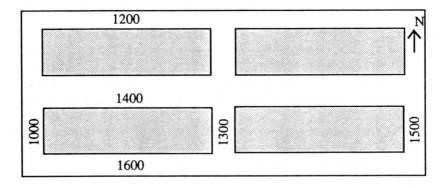

Figure 4.1: Model Environment for Indoor Numbering System

The progression in the numbers assigned to the hallways is usually related to some focal point. The focal point of a numbering system is that point from which all numbered patterns originate. For example, the focal point would be located in the northwest corner of the building if the room and/or hallway numbers become progressively larger as one moves south (i.e., 1200 in the north, 1400 in the middle, and 1600 in the south) and east (i.e., 1100 in the west, 1300 in the middle, and 1500 in the east). The first digit in the hallway number may relate to the floor on which the hallway is located. For example, the 1100 hallway is on the first floor and is directly below the 2100 hallway, which is directly below the 3100 hallway.

The particular room number is determined by its distance from the focal point and rules governing odd/even designation. In some cases, the odd/even designation may serve to identify the specific wall on which the room is located (i.e., odd numbers on the east wall of the odd-numbered hallways and the south wall of the even-numbered hallways). This particular information may be gained as the traveler attempts to identify the location of specific rooms within a building.

Solicitation Questions

The traveler determines the exact location of a particular room by asking:

1. *What is the room number?* The room number is related to a hallway if possible. For example, 1307 is located on the 1300 hallway. The 1300 hallway is the middle corridor (i.e., between 1100 and 1500), on the first floor, and it runs north and south.

2. *On what side of the hallway is it located?* This question is asked to

   (a) locate the room,
   (b) help develop an understanding of the number progression, or

(c)   to check the quality of the answers being provided if that progression is already known.

In our example, an answer of either east or west could be correct since the 1300 hallway runs north and south. East is the correct answer in this case, since an odd/even designation is used, and the odd numbers in this particular building are located on the east and south side of the corridors. Therefore, 1307 must be located on the east wall.

3. *How many doors is it from the nearest corner?* The answer to this question

    (a)   provides the traveler with exact location information,
    (b)   confirms his understanding of the progression of the numbering system, and
    (c)   may alert him to exceptions in that system.

In this case, 1307 should be the fourth door (i.e., 1301, 1303, 1305, and 1307) from the corner since the numbers progress by twos in buildings using odd/even systems.

4. *What is the name of the nearest intersecting hallway?* The answer to this question helps determine the intersection from which the search for the room will start. In the example, the 1200 hallway would be the nearest intersecting corridor. Therefore, the traveler would know he should go to the corner where the 1200 and 1300 hallways intersect.

5. *What direction is the room from the nearest intersecting hallway?* The answer should confirm knowledge about the progression of the numbering system and the general layout of the building. The answer in the example would be south. Therefore, it is known that 1307 is the fourth door on the east wall of the 1300 hallway, south of the 1200 hallway. To get there, the traveler would first locate the corner of 1200 and 1300 and then proceed south to the fourth door.

A general understanding and familiarization with a building may be gained as the traveler builds up information concerning the exact location of a number of rooms within a building. The rules of the layout of the building become apparent as do the exceptions. Exceptions to the rule often prove to be as informative as the rules themselves.

Shops located within Business and Semi-Business Areas

Solicitation procedures similar to that described above work equally well in the outdoor environment. Addresses are sought rather than room numbers, and the questions used are somewhat different because of differences found between indoor and outdoor environments and numbering systems. One of the basic differences between environments is the relative lack of ease in crossing streets as compared to hallways. Therefore, more emphasis is put on locating the exact corner from which the search for an objective will begin. This corner is referred to as a directional corner and is identified in relation to both the perpendicular and the parallel street. As a result, two directions are given. For example, if an objective is located on the south side of one street (i.e., the parallel street), and is east of the nearest intersecting street (i.e., the perpendicular street), we would identify its exact location relative to the southeast corner of the nearest intersection.

Self-directed Search

A blind traveler can familiarize himself with a business district, plaza or mall with little help from the sighted public. The traveler begins at a given intersection and trails the store front to an entrance. The name of the store is obtained and remembered. The traveler continues on building his knowledge of store names, entrances and their physical characteristics. The basic process is cumulative. However, the traveler can choose to group the stores if there are more than four or five to remember. Usually a logical break in the continuity of the stores or the environment is used for this purpose. A number of entrances are grouped together and remembered as a unit. The traveler then works on the relationship of those stores to one another. After all the elements have been successfully committed to memory, the traveler moves on to the next unit or group of entrances. As a result, the specific location of any objective is related to the unit it is contained within, and the unit's position is remembered in relation to the other units and their relative position from the intersections bordering the area explored.

The names of the entrances can be obtained from the business itself by entering every or every other business and inquiring, or from a sighted helper. In this case, anyone who can read can serve as the informant. The informant can also serve as an aid in memory by confirming the traveler's information during verbal review.

This same strategy may also be used in malls and plazas. Often, the traveler culls down the information gained to include only those stores or entrances of interest. The names of those which will not be used are forgotten or, at least, not actively remembered.

5

Cane Techniques

═══════════════════

THE LONG CANE

The cane has long been recognized as an effective aid to mobility. Historically, persons who are blind have used walking-sticks, staffs, canes and various other environment-probing devices to assist them in getting around their environment. Today, there are various types of canes in use which have been developed to meet the variety of needs and preferences of visually impaired people. The most common are the long cane, the folding or collapsible cane, the support or orthopedic cane, and the identification cane.

The long cane is the most effective and efficient mobility aid yet devised for safe, independent travel for the majority of visually impaired people (Farmer, 1980). If used properly, the long cane will provide the traveler with approximately one meter of warning of obstacles or drop-offs in the path of travel. The long cane also provides adequate lower-body protection while transmitting information regarding the walking surface (i.e., texture and quality). The cane does not, however, afford protection above the waist.

The long cane (also called the prescription cane or typhlo cane) has proven to be the aid of choice for the standard O&M training program. This cane serves three primary purposes:

(1)   it affords the traveler protection from drop-offs and obstacles in the path of travel,

(2)   it is used to obtain information from the environment, and as such extends the traveler's tactual sense,

(3)   it identifies the traveler as being blind or visually impaired.

In addition, the cane is made quite visible for added safety (Elliott & Kuyk, 1992; Franck, 1990).

The long cane is so-named due to its length. The length of the cane is individually prescribed based upon the height of the individual, the speed he typically walks, and the length of stride used. As a rule of thumb, the cane length extends to

(a)   five centimeters above the base of the sternum when held vertically in front of the body, or

(b)   just beneath the arm pit when held to the side.

The cane should be made somewhat longer if the person travels with a rapid pace and/or has a long stride. Conversely, the cane may be shortened if the traveler has a slow pace, and/or has a short stride.

The way the individual holds the cane when traveling is also a factor in determining its length. When in use the cane should touch the ground where the ball of the foot will land when the foot is brought forward. The length of the cane may be adjusted to ensure that the traveler neither over- nor under-steps his protection (Blasch & De l'Aune, 1992). Hand position may also be adjusted.

Characteristics of the Long Cane

The long cane and methods for its use were first developed following World War II, by Richard Hoover and staff at Valley Forge Hospital, which later, in 1948, became Hine's Veterans Hospital. In 1964 the Veterans' Administration published *Specifications for the Long Cane* (Veterans' Administration, 1964).

This publication was the basis for the standards adopted for the long cane by the National Academy of Sciences in 1971 (Farmer, 1980).

The long cane is made up of a shaft, a grip, a tip, and sometimes a crook. It should be individually sized to ensure that there is sufficient length to probe the environment and provide coverage when traveling, but not interfere with the individual's freedom of movement. The shaft should

(a)   be straight with a slight taper from grip to tip,
(b)   be rigid, but as light as possible,
(c)   have low wind resistance, low conductivity of thermal and electric energy, but high conductivity of tactual information,
(d)   be well balanced, durable, and relatively quiet.

The long cane should be highly visible, while maintaining an acceptable appearance (National Academy of Sciences Proceedings, cited in Farmer, 1980).

THE DIAGONAL TECHNIQUE

The diagonal cane technique is a very practical and easily learned procedure for traveling in familiar, controlled environments. It is therefore often introduced early in the training program to provide the student with the opportunity to move about the facility safely and meet some immediate needs. This is especially true in residential programs where students have to fend for themselves in the evening and on weekends. However, the use of this procedure should be strictly limited to controlled, familiar environments since it does not protect both sides of the body equally well, or locate drop-offs consistently.

This technique may be used in uncontrolled environments if it is used in conjunction with a human guide, or by persons with enough usable vision to compensate for the lack of protection afforded by the cane. In fact, this technique is often preferred by persons with low vision who wish to carry a cane for identification, and/or use the cane selectively to meet various task or environmental demands.

The diagonal cane technique is often introduced after the self-protective procedures and before the touch technique. This procedure gives the student the opportunity to travel quite freely in the training environment. As a result, the instructor may continue to work on the student's orientation long before the more complex touch technique can be mastered.

The diagonal technique is retained in the individual's travel repertoire after the touch technique has been mastered, to be used selectively in controlled, familiar environments.

The Standard Technique

Objectives

1. To enable the individual to travel independently in a familiar, controlled environment.

2. To provide an unobtrusive procedure for moving through an environment congested with pedestrian traffic.

3. To provide a suitable technique for persons who wish to carry a cane for identification or selective uses but do not require the long cane for protection from obstacles or drop-offs in the path of travel.

Procedure

1. The cane is grasped in one of three ways:

   (a) *The standard grip.* The hand is held in much the same way as is done when offering it to shake hands. The index finger is extended and the thumb up. The grip of the cane is placed along the palm of the hand and the index finger. The index finger is parallel to the cane grip pointing down the shaft, the remaining fingers are then wrapped around the grip, and the thumb is brought down next to the index finger and placed on top and to the side of the grip.

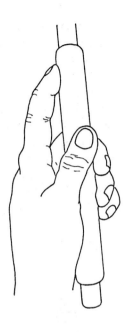

This method is preferred by most people. It is the method used in the touch technique. As such, it allows for an easy transition from one technique to the next. Pointing with the index finger is natural and tends to help the traveler form an accurate perception of the location of the tip.

(b)   *The original grip.* The cane is grasped so the thumb is parallel to the grip of the cane pointing down the shaft toward the tip. The back of the hand faces up and the fingers are flexed around the grip. The cane is rotated so that the crook is forward and over the knuckles of the hand. This method of grasping the cane was originally developed for use with the diagonal cane technique after World War II. It offered protection to the hand through the positioning of the crook, which was often needed due to burns and other wounds experienced by many veterans. The position of the tip is controlled by the thumb.

(c)   *The pencil grip.* The cane is grasped like a pencil between the index finger and the thumb as it rests on the middle finger. The remaining two fingers are curled down and relaxed. This method of grasping the cane appears more casual than the other options.

2. The hand is held forward and just out to the side of the hip.

3. The arm is flexed at the shoulder until the hand is approximately waist height and forward of the body by 20-30cm. This position provides maximum frontal protection and reaction time.

4. The forearm is inwardly rotated until the palm of the hand is facing down.

5. The crook of the cane may be positioned

(a)   outward and to the side, adding extra protection to the shoulder away from the tip,

(b)   up over the knuckles to provide protection to the back of the hand, or

(c)   inward, rotated up behind the wrist so that it is out of the way and therefore does not contact objects in the environment.

6. The shaft of the cane is positioned diagonally across the body from the hand grasping the cane to the tip.

7. The tip is positioned forward of the grip and approximately one inch beyond the outside shoulder. As a result, the cane provides complete frontal protection covering the body from shoulder to shoulder.

8. The tip of the cane may be

   (a)   raised just above the floor to avoid sticking in carpets or cracks, or
   (b)   kept in contact with the floor and slid along the surface.

   Maintaining constant or intermittent contact with the walking surface provides the traveler with some additional information and acts as an aid in the detection of drop-offs.

9. The cane may be held in either hand depending upon

   (a)   the preference of the traveler, and
   (b)   the placement of objects within the environment.

Limitations

The diagonal cane technique provides adequate protection for moving about controlled environments. However, there are a number of limitations inherent in this procedure which restrict its use to controlled, familiar environments if it must be relied upon for protection from objects within the environment or the detection of drop-offs (Hill & Ponder, 1976).

1. *Detection of drop-offs.* Drop-offs may only be detected with consistency if

   (a)   the tip is in contact with the floor, and
   (b)   the drop-off is directly in front of the traveler, or
   (c)   the drop-off is located to the side the tip is on.

   When traveling in familiar environments, the traveler can anticipate the location of a drop-off. As a result he can ensure that the cane is held in the hand which offers the best chance for locating the drop-off, lower the tip to the surface and endeavor to approach the drop-off in a perpendicular fashion.

2. *Protection from objects in the travel environment.* When using the diagonal cane technique, the body is unprotected from low objects on the side away from the cane tip. Such common objects as waste baskets, foot-stools and benches can elude the protection afforded by the cane. In familiar environments these objects may be anticipated and the traveler may shift the cane to the hand which affords the best potential to detect them. Also the cane may pass over low objects when making facing movements (i.e., 90-degree turn) and the traveler should clear the path of travel by sweeping the cane in an arc before moving out after making a facing movement. As with other cane techniques, no protection is afforded from obstacles above the waist which do not extend downward in the vertical plane.

Teaching Considerations

Introduction of the diagonal cane technique affords the student the opportunity to fully develop straight-line travel skills, while moving about the environment independently. Typically, the technique is introduced in a wide, uncluttered hallway with the student travelling the length of it. The objective is the perpendicular wall at the end. This is used to provide the student with

(a)   a tactual indication that the objective has been met,
(b)   an occasion to contact an object within the path of travel, and
(c)   an opportunity to develop a kinesthetic awareness of the length of the hallway.

Repeated trials are necessary to develop skill and competence.

Students often have difficulty keeping the tip from riding up too high at first. This is probably due to anxiety. This problem may be avoided by introducing the technique with the tip in contact with the floor initially, and having the student raise it only after confidence has been gained. The standard or original grip is introduced initially. The pencil grip may be introduced after the student has demonstrated competence with the diagonal technique.

The instructor will generally walk backwards in front of the student for the initial trials. This is done to

(a)   give the instructor an opportunity to observe the student's technique from the front,
(b)   provide auditory and verbal cues to the student to facilitate straight-line travel, and
(c)   clear the way for the student of unplanned contact with pedestrians or objects in the environment.

While in front of the student, the instructor observes the hand to ensure that it has not drifted toward midline, thus reducing coverage on the grip side and extending it unnecessarily on the tip side.

After a number of trials, the instructor begins to move around the student observing the diagonal technique from a number of angles. The tip is observed from the side to ensure that it has not dropped back to the same plane as the crook. The hand is also observed from this angle to ensure that it is forward and has not dropped back towards the student. If either of these happen, forward coverage and reaction time is greatly reduced. The tip and the crook should be just visible when observed from behind.

The student should be asked to travel with the cane in either hand. Repeated trials of straight-line travel should continue until the student demonstrates competence with the standard technique with either hand.

Contacting and Exploring Objects

Objective

To enable the traveler to safely and efficiently contact and examine an object.

Procedure

1. When contact is made, the traveler stops and holds his relative position to the object.

2. If the traveler has no desire to explore the object:

    (a) contact is broken with the object by pulling the cane back slightly,

    (b) the area to the side of the object is swept with the cane to find a clear path of travel, and

    (c) the traveler continues to the intended destination.

3. If exploration is desired:

    (a) the cane remains anchored against the object at the point of contact,

    (b) the cane is inwardly (i.e., toward self) rotated in the hand bringing it to a vertical position while changing to a modified pencil grip (i.e., the cane is held vertically between the thumb and index finger), or

(c)   the palm of the hand is outwardly rotated bringing the cane to a vertical position, the grip modified but not changed substantially.

As this is done, the arm is brought across the body for protection and the cane is held vertical to the point of contact.

4. The traveler maintains this position taking care not to turn towards the cane tip. The point of reference is thus maintained.

5. The traveler steps up to the object.

6. The grip is pushed forward to determine the relative height of the object. The cane may be raised slightly in the case of very low objects.

7. The cane is lifted up off the floor and moved horizontally, while remaining in a vertical position, to determine the width of the object. The cane may be changed from hand to hand to fully explore the area on either side of the traveler if necessary.

8. The traveler may slide the free hand down the cane to the object to explore it tactually. If the object is low, the traveler may wish to squat in the space currently occupied in order to accomplish this. In this way the head and body are protected from unexpected contact.

The student should be encouraged to explore objects initially with the cane held in a vertical position rather than with the free hand. The hands and fingers are protected from jagged edges, broken glass and closing doors.

Locating and Passing Through Doorways

Objective

To enable the traveler to safely and efficiently negotiate a closed door.

Procedure

1. Upon contacting the door, the traveler anchors the cane and then pushes it up to a vertical position while rotating it in his hand to change to a modified pencil grip, as is done when any object is contacted.

2. The cane is pushed forward until it comes into contact with the door. The traveler stays back at arm's length from the door to avoid having it opened into him.

3. The traveler then

   (a)   contacts the door with the closed fist of his free hand, and/or
   (b)   slides a foot forward to provide a bumper for the door if it is opened toward the traveler.

4. The cane is lifted slightly and moved horizontally from side to side to locate the handle. The cane may be transferred from

hand to hand at midline for this purpose. Some pressure is exerted on the door when the jam has been located. This is done to determine if the door can be opened (pushed) in this manner. The cane is maintained in a vertical position. The shaft is used to locate the handle since it covers so much more space than the hand. The surface of the door is explored by the cane as a means of protecting the hand.

5. Once the handle has been located, the free hand is slid down the shaft to the handle and the door is opened.

6. The area to be walked through is cleared by a sweep of the cane before proceeding through the door using the diagonal technique.

Teaching Considerations

The protective qualities of these procedures are important and may need emphasis. The student should be encouraged to execute these procedures as quickly and efficiently as possible to lessen the time spent in a fairly vulnerable position. The student should also be encouraged to keep a distance from the door while looking for the handle, and to keep the free hand in contact with it, or the foot forward to avoid being hit by it. The cane should be employed when exploring the doors surface to avoid having the fingers shut in a self-closing door.

The student should be aware that doors (fire doors particularly) are hung so that they must be pushed when exiting a building and pulled when entering. Therefore, students should be able to anticipate the action of the door, and use this information to confirm or re-establish their orientation.

Trailing Technique

Objectives

1. To enable the traveler to locate specific objectives along a wall or building line.

2. To enable the traveler to maintain a straight line of travel.

3. To enable the traveler to maintain contact with the environment while traveling through space.

Procedure

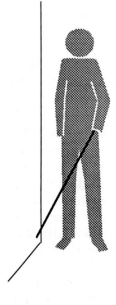

1. The traveler faces the desired direction, positioned parallel to and near the trailing surface. The cane is held in the hand opposite the surface to be trailed. The traveler should remain 10-20cm from the trailing surface. The cane extends across the body to the surface providing full frontal protection. Some reaction time is lost if the hand is not brought forward to compensate for the lateral extension of the cane.

2. The tip of the cane is placed just above the floor in light contact with the trailing surface.

3. The traveler proceeds along the surface mentally projecting a straight line and maintaining light contact with the cane tip.

Teaching Considerations

Trailing is most commonly used for traveling short distances and may require the use of either hand. As a result, this procedure is often introduced along a wall with a number of doors. The student is asked to trail to the first door, locate it and return to the starting point. He is then asked to move on to the second door and back, the third door and so on. In this way, the student gets sufficient practice with both hands.

Maintaining a position near the wall is important, as is remaining behind the protection of the cane. There is a tendency to reach to the wall, rather than to move in alongside it. When this happens, reaction time, frontal protection and protection to the side opposite the trailing surface are all reduced. As a result, the instructor should encourage the traveler to keep the cane forward and to follow the tip. The instructor should also check the hand holding the cane to be sure it is maintained in front of the hip to avoid losing protection on that side of the body. Generally, it is prudent to reduce the pace and avoid using the free hand in the trailing process unless it is needed for fine discrimination when locating a specific objective.

Once competence with this technique has been demonstrated, the instructor can move on to having the student find specific objectives within the environment and travel 'L', 'U' and 'Z'-shaped patterns using the diagonal cane technique predominantly and the diagonal trailing technique as required. When traveling patterns, the student is expected to use kinesthetic awareness and auditory cues to locate intersecting hallways and turn on them. The trailing technique provides the student with the technique needed for moving along the hall to the intersection if the turn had been attempted either too early or too late. Missing the intersection is not treated like a mistake. Rather, these occasions are treated as opportunities for the student to employ the trailing technique selectively to recover and find the intersection.

The student is also asked to travel to specific objectives. These objectives are located near intersections initially. As a result, the student is expected to travel to a given intersection, locate the wall on which the objective is located, trail to the intersection, and then trail back to the specified objective. This routine is carried out to ensure that the door found is indeed the first, second or third from the corner. The trailing technique should be used selectively. Objectives are selected to encourage this concept. Likewise, the student is encouraged to use the trailing procedure to establish a straight line, or re-establish his place in the environment.

Miscellaneous

Use of the Diagonal Cane When Traveling with a Guide

Frequently, the traveler will be in possession of the cane when using a human guide to travel. The cane may simply be carried to the side and out of the way when walking with an experienced and trusted guide, or be used to provide the traveler with protection if needed. A modified diagonal cane technique is used for this purpose.

Objective

To provide the traveler with an efficient means of carrying a cane while traveling with a human guide and provide additional protection if required.

Procedure

1. The guide and traveler assume their basic human guide positions. The cane is held in the free hand and may be tucked up under the arm and out of the way, or held in the basic diagonal position with the following modifications:

(a)   the shaft is grasped below the grip,
(b)   the grip is against or in line with the back of the forearm, and
(c)   the hand is held at the side in a natural position with the tip forward at the traveler's midline.

The tip may be lowered to the travel surface when a drop-off is anticipated.

2. The cane may be held in the guide hand when negotiating doors. This is done to free the other hand for handling the door. In this case, the cane is placed between the thumb and the guide's arm or held in a pencil grip with the back of the hand in contact with the guide arm.

3. When traveling in a car, the cane is brought in after the traveler has been seated and is placed between the legs with the crook resting on or near the shoulder, or is placed between the traveler and the passenger door. For longer trips, the cane may be placed in the back seat or the trunk (boot).

Cane Placement

There are numerous occasions when the cane needs to be placed out of the way, yet be kept handy for use when needed. The cane may be hung by its crook or strap on a hook or placed vertically in a corner against the wall. When seated, the cane may be placed parallel to pedestrian traffic against the front edge or side of a sofa or chair, or diagonally underneath a chair or table. People often place their foot on the cane to keep track of it and to keep it from being kicked away by someone walking by. The cane may also be held vertically between the knees when seated if it is not convenient to place it on the floor. When standing, the cane should be placed parallel to and near the body, or may be tucked under the arm at the side of the body.

Ascending and Descending Stairways

The stairway techniques can be introduced as a transition between the diagonal technique and the touch technique. In fact, these procedures more closely resemble the diagonal and therefore seem to logically belong here in the instructional sequence. However, it must be remembered that the diagonal can only be depended upon for identifying drop-offs when their presence can be anticipated (i.e., controlled and familiar environments). As a result, some instructors prefer to present this skill area only after the basic touch technique has been introduced, which can be relied upon to consistently locate drop-offs and thus stairs anywhere within the immediate path of travel. Therefore, the decision to introduce this procedure as a transition between the diagonal and the touch is dependent upon the instructor's philosophical viewpoint, and the training environment used. The environment must be one that

(a)   has a travel surface which does not interfere with the progress of the tip as it is slid along the floor,
(b)   has controlled access to drop-offs and stairwells, and
(c)   has features which would prove beneficial to the instructional program if they could be accessed by the use of these procedures.

A good example of such an environment would be one which has multiple floors that are accessed by stairwells separated from the main building by firedoors. This environment would be considered to be controlled for stairs if they were only encountered out in the stairwell, and the stairwell could only be entered by passing through firedoors. Therefore, the presence of the stairs could always be anticipated and the traveler could take the appropriate measures to ensure that the drop-off was located while using the diagonal cane technique. The fact that the building had multiple floors would provide the instructor with the opportunity to challenge the student's orientation skills through the use of multifloor travel experiences, develop generalizations across floors, and continue to introduce new objectives while providing adequate time for repetition with the cane skills yet to be introduced.

Ascending Stairs

Objective

To enable the traveler to safely and independently locate and ascend stairs.

Procedure

1. The traveler uses environmental cues and landmarks in an attempt to approach the stairs in a perpendicular fashion. If using the diagonal cane technique, the tip should be in contact with the travel surface. The traveler's weight may be shifted back and the pace decreased in anticipation of the stairs.

2. As the riser is located

   (a)   the tip of the cane is anchored against the edge of the first step, and
   (b)   the cane is inwardly rotated in the hand bringing it to a vertical position while changing the grip to

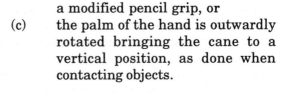

a modified pencil grip, or

(c)   the palm of the hand is outwardly rotated bringing the cane to a vertical position, as done when contacting objects.

3. The cane is brought to midline. The traveler may step up to the cane positioning the toes against the riser, or remain back from the stairs as preferred. The cane may be moved from side to side, as is done when exploring doors, in order to

(a)   determine position at the stairway, and/or

(b)   establish perpendicular alignment to the stairs.

4. The arm is flexed at the shoulder and is nearly parallel to the floor. As a result, the cane is drawn up along the riser. The grip should be adjusted, moving down the shaft to ensure that the tip is in contact with the top of the second or third riser depending on the height of the traveler and length of the cane.

5. The cane is held diagonally to provide protection to the traveler.

6. The traveler shifts his weight forward and ascends the stairs with the tip lightly touching the facing of each step. The position of the arm must be maintained rather well in order to be confident that the tip will touch each step briefly. If the

arm is raised, the step may be missed. Conversely, if the arm is dropped, the tip will drag along the riser, becoming cumbersome to the traveler.

7. The traveler progresses up the stairs until the tip swings clear of the last step. At this point, the traveler pauses, adjusts the grip to resume using either the diagonal or touch technique, clears for the first stride or forward step and continues. There should be one or two steps left to ascend, depending upon the initial positioning of the cane. It is important to move the cane forward with the first forward step by the traveler, in order not to 'catch-up' to the cane.

Descending Stairs

Objective

To enable the traveler to safely and independently locate and descend stairs.

Procedure

1. The traveler uses environmental cues and landmarks in an attempt to approach the stairs in a perpendicular fashion. If using the diagonal cane technique, the tip should be in contact with the travel surface. The weight may be shifted back and the pace decreased in anticipation.

2. When the drop-off is located, the tip of the cane is anchored against the edge of the step as the cane is brought to a vertical position at midline.

3. The traveler may step up to the cane with his toes at the edge, or remain back as prefered. He then squares-off to the step using

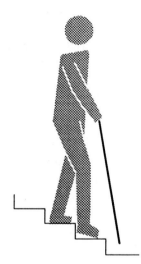

   (a)   tactual information provided through the balls of his feet, and/or
   (b)   the checking procedure described for ascending stairs.

4. The cane is brought to a modified diagonal with the tip

   (a)   positioned in front of the foot opposite to the grip, and
   (b)   extended out and down so that it is forward of the edge of the second step.

   The cane's position should be

   (a)   no wider than the traveler's body,
   (b)   extended down to facilitate timely detection of the landing, and
   (c)   extended out to avoid striking steps as the traveler descends.

5. The weight should be shifted back while the traveler descends with the cane held in the fixed position with the tip making no contact with the stairs.

6. There should be one step left to negotiate when the tip strikes the landing. At this time, the traveler steps down, clears the path of travel and continues in the desired direction.

Teaching Considerations

The environment used to introduce the stairway procedures should be as standard and predictable as possible, lacking irregularities that produce undue anxiety and errors in technique. Stairwells are often used when introducing these techniques since they provide a relatively standard environment with limited access and definite physical boundaries.

A point of reference, usually the fire door, is used when entering the stairwell to facilitate orientation. The student may be asked to explore the stairwell area to establish the position of the stairs from the door. When using the diagonal cane technique, the tip should be in constant contact with the surface in this environment to detect drop-offs. The instructor should be positioned on the second or third stair down the descending stairway to provide protection to the student.

The student is usually given ample opportunity to approach the stairs before beginning to introduce the stairway techniques and may also be given the opportunity to explore the stairs to determine the width and height or depth of the steps using the contacting objects procedures. The student may also establish a perpendicular alignment to the stairs by drawing the cane tip along the edge of the step from midline out to arm's length on either side and/or rocking forward on the balls of his feet at the top of descending stairs. These procedures may be eliminated as competence is gained, or if handrails are used.

Generally, the instructor will introduce ascending stairs prior to descending stairs, as the former is less anxiety provoking than the latter. The instructor should initially be positioned just behind the student while ascending, in the event of the student losing his balance. This does not usually occur as long as the center of gravity is kept forward and a normal pace is maintained.

During descent the instructor is initially positioned two to three steps below the student to ensure safety. This position is maintained as the student descends. The instructor walks backwards down the stairs with one hand on the railing. A three-point position (i.e., one foot forward, one back, and the hand on the rail) is maintained to provide leverage if the student does need to be helped. Some instructors prefer to not walk backwards and simply precede the student by a step, angled slightly toward the traveler.

The opportunity to use the handrail may be important for some students. The instructor will eventually encourage the student to negotiate stairs without the use of handrails. However, there are some students who will simply never want to do this.

THE TOUCH TECHNIQUE

The touch technique (or its variant, the constant-contact technique) is the most used and most important of the cane techniques. An independent cane traveler will probably use this technique over 90 per cent of the time. The touch technique is designed to provide protection from objects in the path of travel and detect drop-offs (Hill & Ponder, 1976). This system works equally well on either side of the body. Anticipation is not essential to function. Therefore, the traveler is not restricted to familiar or controlled environments when traveling with this technique.

The cane tip contacts the surface to be stepped in while the foot is back. Therefore, the foot is always brought forward and placed in an area previously occupied by the cane tip (Blasch & De L'Aune, 1992). The fact that this is done contralaterally (i.e., done while the foot is back) provides the traveler with approximately one meter to react to contact or lack of it (e.g., drop-offs).

Instruction with this technique usually begins in a controlled indoor environment which is conducive to the development of the technique. Long corridors with smooth floors and unobstructed space provide an ideal learning environment. A large all-purpose room or gymnasium would also serve the purpose. If no ideal area is available, a long smooth driveway, sidewalk or cemented area may suffice. Whatever area is used, the student should be able to concentrate on the development of the technique without being greatly concerned with safety needs or orientation.

The Standard Technique

Objectives

1. To provide the traveler with a technique which gives maximum protection and information.

2. To provide the traveler with a consistent means of detecting drop-offs.

3. To promote independent travel in all environments.

Procedure

1. The cane is grasped with the hand held forward as is done when shaking hands. The index finger is extended parallel along the grip, pointing down the shaft toward the tip. The thumb is positioned diagonally across the top of the grip. The remaining fingers are curled under the grip providing support. The top of the grip should come to rest at the top of the palm. The crook should be facing down. Many grips (i.e., reminder grips) have a flattened side which is situated in such a way to ensure that the crook is pointing down when the index finger is laid alongside it.

2. The arm is flexed at the shoulder until the hand is waist height. The arm is fully extended in a firm position and the elbow is flexed slightly (not locked). The upper-arm may rest against the body.

3. The hand is positioned at the center of the body, providing

   (a)   a point of reference for the technique,
   (b)   a symetrical arc,
   (c)   equal coverage of both sides of the body, and
   (d)   maximal frontal protection.

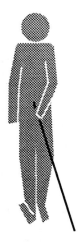

4. The wrist is outwardly rotated so that the prominent bones at the base of the thumb face upward and the back of the hand faces the side.

5. The cane is moved from side to side by the flexion of the wrist. This movement describes an arc with the tip, which touches the floor approximately 2.5 cm outside the widest part of the body (i.e., shoulder or hips). The tip is raised slightly as the cane moves from one extreme to the next to avoid sticking and unneccesary feedback.

6. The cane movement is synchronized with the feet, resulting in an alternating foot-cane pattern (i.e., as the right foot strikes the floor, the cane is striking the floor in front of the left foot). As a result, the area in which the foot will be placed is cleared when it is still back. This pattern

allows for as much reaction time as possible, which is equal to one full stride.

Teaching Considerations

The various components of the touch technique are initially introduced and practiced with the student stationary. The hand is centered, the wrist is moved back and forth, and the width of the arc is established. Verbal instruction and physical prompting is used. The student is asked to practice these skills before beginning to walk with the technique. The cane is held in the dominant hand. There is no need to practice using it in both hands, as is done with the diagonal.

The instructor will work on shaping the components of the technique to an acceptable level as the student travels the hallway. The instructor may walk backwards down the hall, providing the student with feedback about the technique and verbal cues for straight line. Each component will be emphasized separately to avoid confusion and overload. The order in which the components are isolated for emphasis may vary from instructor to instructor, but most often follows one of two sequences.

In the first, the instructor will often concentrate on having the hand centered with proper wrist motion and not worry about the width of the arc or the rhythm and coordination of the feet. As skill is demonstrated with this, the instructor will begin to ensure that the arc is neither too wide nor too narrow. The instructor may then begin to concentrate on getting the student into step. In this case, it is easiest if the student starts with the cane in front of the foot opposite the hand holding the cane. The student is instructed to start off stepping out with this foot while beginning the swing of the cane as he goes. The cane strike at footfall must be coordinated so that the cane strikes the surface in front of the foot that is back. It is often easiest to work on coordination after rhythm has been established, which often happens naturally after the student has had sufficient opportunity to travel swinging the cane in an arc.

In the second, the sequence would be ordered so that rhythm

must be established before moving on to other components. Rhythm is the glue which holds the technique together and until it is established, the coordination of feet and cane are antagonistic. Proper rhythm ensures remaining in step and gives an overall feeling of harmony between the cane and the feet. The instructor now proceeds to centered hand with the upper arm properly placed against the body as a reference point. This is followed by an equal arc and then refinement of the overall technique.

The instructor moves around the student in order to observe the technique from varying positions. The motion of the wrist, position of the hand, and the coordination of the cane and foot can be observed from the front. The width of the arc can be observed from the back. The placement of the cane tip and the fall of the foot can be seen from the side. In this case, the instructor may pick out some lines naturally occuring in the environment and use them to determine if the student is either over or understepping the cane. Final adjustments to cane length may be made based on these observations.

The instructor may now begin to emphasize a quiet technique and watch for the height of the arc to ensure that it is appropriate. It is important that proficiency be developed with these techniques at this point, since it is very difficult to change style at a later date. As a result, the instructor must promote good technique and convince the student of its necessity.

There is no substitute for proficiency. It is only through a polished, well developed technique that the traveler will become sensitive to subtle information available through the cane. The experienced and proficient cane traveler can perceive slight changes in texture as well as slight deviations in gradient.

As proficiency with these techniques develop, the instructor may expand the environment of travel and shift the responsibility for orientation and personal safety to the student. The student has the skills to handle doorways, trail with a diagonal technique to find specific objectives, and handle stairs for multi-floor travel.

The Touch-and-Slide Technique

Objectives

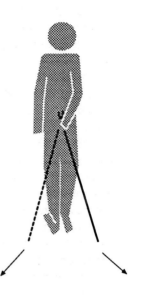

1. To provide a more continuous read-out of the environment.

2. To provide earlier warning of drop-offs.

3. To enhance the detection of the subtle changes in texture.

Procedure

1. The cane tip is touched down at approximately 30 degrees past midline.

2. The tip remains in contact with the walking surface as it slides 20-25 cm to the lateral extent of the arc.

3. The return of the cane is slightly quicker.

Teaching Considerations

The touch-and-slide may be introduced any time after competency with the touch technique has been demonstrated. The instructor may introduce it quite early for those students who are having little difficulty coordinating the touch technique. The touch-and-slide may become their primary technique. For others it may be introduced later for detection of blended curbs or texture changes. The technique may be used situationally or evolve into the primary technique over time.

This technique requires good coordination and is difficult to learn initially. The instructor needs to time its introduction carefully, or use instead the constant contact technique.

The Constant-Contact Technique

The constant contact technique is a variation on the touch technique. The procedures are the same except that the cane is not lifted from the ground at any point within its arc. Proponents of this technique suggest that it provides the traveler with 'superior tactual feedback, resulting in the detection of small surface discontinuities and precise location of walkway margins, with obstacle detection equal to that provided by the [standard touch technique] and superior detection of vertical breaks in the walking surface, along with rich textural feedback about the nature of this surface. Much of this advantage is obtained because aspects of the [standard touch technique] and the touch-and-slide technique are combined in one more powerfully comprehensive cane application. Drop-offs, sharp gradients, and blended curbs are detected earlier, thus improving reaction time, because the edge of the discontinuity may be contacted at any point of the cane arc, rather than just at its outer reaches, as the cane is slid from forehand to backhand to the extension of the arc at parallel points just outside the shoulders' (Fisk, 1986, p. 999).

A mushroom tip or other rounded-off tip is recommended when using this technique to eliminate sticking and prolong tip wear. Locating drop-offs with the constant contact technique does not rely upon rhythm and step as much as the standard technique. As a result, this technique may prove to be particularly useful for persons with an extremely slow pace or very short stride. Many instructors are employing the constant-contact technique and mushroom tip with elderly travelers. Fisk (1986) suggests it may provide some advantages over the standard touch technique to all travelers.

TRAILING TECHNIQUES

Trailing with a touch technique can be accomplished using the two-point touch, the three-point touch, or the touch-and-drag techniques. The two-point touch is the basic technique and is used for trailing vertical (e.g., walls) or horizontal (e.g., grass lines) surfaces. The three-point procedure is needed to detect doors which do not open at the travel surface, or intersecting sidewalks which are present above the travel plane. In this case, the third point of contact is added to locate these specific objectives. The touch-and-drag is used to trail the edge of a drop-off from a raised position, or to detect a seam, ridge, or texture change, parallel to the line of travel. In this case, the cane is kept in constant contact from the outside shoulder to the edge.

Objectives

1. To enable the traveler to locate specific objectives along a wall, building or grass line.

2. To enable the traveler to maintain a straight line of travel.

3. To enable the traveler to maintain contact with the environment while traveling through space.

Procedure: **Two-Point Touch**

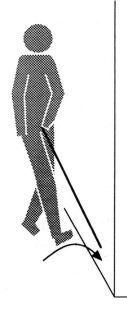

1. The traveler faces the desired direction, positioned parallel to and near the surface.

2. The arc of the cane may be extended about 15-25cm to the side being trailed.

3. The cane should make consistent but light contact with the trailing surface each time it is swung to that side.

4. The pace may be slowed to account for the extended arc and decreased reaction time resulting from it.

5. The trailing surface must be checked any time contact is not made to determine if an opening or intersection has been detected. This must be done instantly and habitually. If the traveler has drifted from the intended line, he should avoid extending the arc to compensate, but rather move in closer to the line and continue trailing.

6. The cane does not change hands for trailing surfaces on opposite sides of the body. However, people do have a tendency to drift away from the trailing surface when trailing on the dominant side. This can be avoided if the hand remains centered and the width of the arc is not unduly extended.

Procedure: **Three-Point Touch**

When looking for an opening or an intersecting sidewalk which exists above the plane of travel, a third point of contact is desirable (i.e., three-point touch). The tip

(a) touches the side away from the trailing surface,
(b) contacts the trailing surface to maintain a straight line while trailing, and
(c) is lifted up after striking the trailing surface.

The tip may be moved vertically along the trailing surface for about six inches to locate an opening existing above ground level, or lifted over the curb and placed in the grass above it to locate an intersecting sidewalk.

The pace should be slowed to compensate for this movement.

Travelers often find it most comfortable to pause after striking the trailing surface and wait until the cane begins to move towards the opposite side before resuming travel. In this regard, experienced travelers may use a hesitation stride with the leg opposite the trailing surface, in order to remain in step.

Procedure: **Touch-and-Drag**

Edges extending up in the vertical plane are most often used for trailing. However, the occasion does arise when the edge of a drop-off may also be used (i.e., when moving along a train platform, or other raised area). In this case, a touch-and-drag procedure is used (Uslan, 1990a.; Uslan & Schreibman, 1980).

1. The touch and drag modifies the two-point trailing procedure by leaving the tip in constant contact with the walking surface as it is dragged from the outside shoulder to the edge of trailing surface.

2. The cane is swung back normally to the other side then dragged back to the edge to continue the traditional coverage of the touch technique. In this way, the traveler can maintain a straight line with the edge while being constantly aware of its location. This also works well when trailing a small ridge or seam, perhaps in passing a driveway entrance to a gas station.

Procedure: **Alternate Touch-and-Drag**

1. The traveler straddles the ridge or seam to be followed.

2. The cane tip is dragged to the seam at midline, then lifted to be touched again at the lateral aspect of arc.

3. The return arc to the opposite side is carried out normally.

Teaching Considerations

The two-point trailing technique can be introduced at any time after competence with the touch technique has been demonstrated. At that time, the two-point touch technique would be substituted for the diagonal procedure. A great deal of practice is required with this procedure since consistency in trailing must be established. However, the practice should correspond with its traditional uses. Therefore, students should not be encouraged to travel long distances with it simply to gain practice time.

The student should work on trailing surfaces on either side of his body. Success is more likely when trailing on the side opposite of the cane hand initially. Much practice is required to gain equivalent skill on the other side.

Trailing is used most often to find specific objectives. However, student's should be encouraged to use it to re-establish their line of travel as well. Therefore, when the wall (i.e., in the hallway) or the grass-line (i.e., along a sidewalk) is contacted, the student may be encouraged to maintain that contact for a short and controlled term. Once the line has been established, the student would then step away from it laterally and continue on his way.

The three-point trailing technique may be introduced indoors if features in the training environment warrant it. However, it is most often introduced outdoors as part of the recovery technique for street crossings.

The touch-and-drag can be introduced any time in the training sequence after the touch technique and trailing with it has been introduced. However, it usually is not introduced until quite late in the sequence, due to the type of environment which requires its use.

6

Environmental Sequence and Selection

Success in travel within each environment requires certain prerequisite skills. As a result, the environments used for training are introduced in a specific order. The timing of that introduction is controlled to ensure that the prerequisite skills have been mastered before moving on.

STANDARD SEQUENCE

Typically, indoor environments are used first, then quiet residential, semi-business, and business environments. Indoor environments allow for the introduction of the various techniques without the worries of traffic, uncontrolled drop-offs, or sticking of the cane tip. Sticking tends to pose a major problem to the student when moving into the residential environment. The student must also learn to identify intersecting streets, cross streets, and recover from veers as they occur. A quiet residential environment provides the student with the opportunity to master these skills without having to deal with heavy traffic or traffic light-controlled intersections.

Semi-business environments are often used as a transition from the residential to the business environment. Semi-business environments usually are busier than residential environments, have a variety of sidewalk types, businesses and private homes, and controlled (i.e., traffic light) and uncontrolled intersections.

Business environments generally have busier streets, a greater variety of intersections, traffic patterns, and traffic control devices. They also usually have very wide sidewalks which stretch from building line to curb, and a heavier concentration of pedestrians.

SELECTING THE TRAINING ENVIRONMENT

Selection of the training environment is dependent upon the goal of training, as well as the features present within the available environments. Training for generalization requires the selection of environments with representative features to ensure that skills obtained during training may be transferred elsewhere. Environment-specific instruction does not pose the same requirements. The following discussion is limited to the former goal.

Ideally, indoor environments should have controlled access to stairs, stairways, multiple floors, multiple hallways which intersect, wide and uncluttered hallways, discernible numbering systems, firedoors, more than one set of exit doors, and a number of internal doorways to be used as objectives for travel.

Residential environments should have sidewalks in good repair; a number of streets with light traffic flow, a few streets with moderate flow, and at least one street with relatively heavy traffic flow; sign-controlled and uncontrolled intersections; many dominant curbs and a few blended curbs; a number of driveways and sidewalks leading to private residences; a numbering system representative of the community at large; a number of dominant environmental clues and at least one landmark. Semi-business environments should be an extension of the residential environment along a busier street. They should contain at least one traffic light-controlled intersection; a variety of intersection types; a number of businesses; and at least one sidewalk which stretches from the building (or property) line to the curb. Business environments should contain a number of busy streets; a variety of street types (i.e., one-way, two-way, two-lane, four-lane), intersection types (i.e., T, off-set, roundabouts) and various traffic control devices and patterns (i.e., buzzer, pedestrian light, traffic light, turning arrow, etc.); numerous businesses; at least one street with heavy pedestrian traffic; blended curbs; an open stairway; a bus stop; and access to at least one revolving door, automatic door, elevator, and escalator. Other environments for training may include malls and plazas, department stores, grocery stores, bus and train depots, and airports.

When selecting environments for training, the instructor should attempt to provide the student with a degree of continuity across the various environments. It is often desirable to have at least one street in common across all of the outdoor training environments. Often, the busy street in the residential environment also contains the semi-business environment. It would be ideal if this same street flowed into the business environment as well. The instructor should also attempt to ensure that the general environmental layout is representative. However, it is also important that exceptions to the rule exist within the training environments as well. These exceptions are generally introduced later in the training sequence.

INDOOR ENVIRONMENTS

The human guide, self-protective, positional, diagonal and touch techniques can all be introduced within the indoor environment, as can general orientation and nomenclature. The instructor uses cardinal directions when developing orientation to this environment, numbering systems are introduced, and objectives are located in relation to the nearest intersection. This is done to develop a systematic approach to orientation which is transferable to all environments of travel.

If an appropriate indoor environment is not available for instruction much of the sequence described here may be introduced in the residential environment. Yet appropriate modifications must be made (e.g., introducing constant contact or touch technique in place of the diagonal cane technique) to account for the different demands placed on the traveler by the environments in question. A mushroom or other rounded tip may be used in order to avoid problems with sticking.

Introduction and Home-base

The student is introduced to the layout of the indoor environment using human guide procedures. All lessons emanate from a given point. That starting point usually coincides with the focal point of the numbering system and is used as the home-base for further lessons. The focal point is the place where the numbering system originates (i.e., all numbers increase from that point). The home-base provides the student with a regular starting and ending point for each lesson.

The outer boundary of the environment is introduced initially followed by the intersecting hallways. The hallways are named and the direction they run is established. Numbering systems are then introduced. Specific objectives are located to reinforce the numbering system. The concept of odd and even numbering is introduced if applicable. Major clues and landmarks are established. Finally, the routes are expanded to encompass all floors in the building. Generalization is established across the various floors. Once the rule concerning layout has been established, any exceptions to the rule are identified. The exceptions are used to establish clues and/or landmarks where appropriate.

Orientation to the indoor environment is expanded as the student begins to move independently using the diagonal cane and the touch technique. Specific objectives are located using the various trailing procedures. The nearest intersection to the objective is established then located. The student then trails from the nearest intersection to the objective. This is done to ensure that the student

(a)   uses the procedure selectively,

(b)   keeps track of the fewest number of doorways (e.g., third door south from the southwest corner of a given intersection rather than the eighth door north of the northwest corner of the previous one),

(c)   develops a clear understanding of the information provided by the numbering system, and

(d)   is introduced to a system which is applicable to outdoor environments as well.

As such, the student is prepared for the introduction of directional corners upon moving outdoors.

Travel Patterns

Travel patterns typically move from straight lines to 'L' and 'U' patterns, and on to 'Z's'. This pattern is repeated as the environment is expanded to include the other floors, and again when the diagonal and the touch technique are introduced.

Straight-line trips allow the student to concentrate on the technique being introduced with little or no worries about orientation. Patterns other than straight lines require the student to turn into intersecting hallways. The student, therefore, must be kinesthetically aware in order to determine when to begin looking for the intersection, and auditorially attuned to be able to find it. When traveling independently, the student must be capable of trailing if the intersecting hallway is not located auditorially.

'L' patterns link two straight lines. 'U' patterns add a leg to the 'L' requiring the student to maintain orientation while backtracking. A 'U' pattern can be closed up to form a square/ rectangle or expanded to form the more complicated 'Z'.

When traveling in a straight line the student may be required to go from the intersection of the 100 and 200 corridors to the intersection of the 100 and 600 corridors. In order to do this the student must travel south on the 100 corridor. An 'L' pattern may require the student to go from the corner of the 100 and 200 corridors to the corner of the 600 and 500. The student could travel east on the 200 to the 500 and south on the 500 to the 600, or south on the 100 to the 600 and east on the 600 to the 500. A 'U' pattern may require the student to go from the 100 and 200 to the 200 and 500 without traveling on the 200. The student could then travel south on the 100 to the 400, east on the 400 to the 500, and north on the 500 to the 200. A 'Z' pattern could be created by having the student travel from the corner of the 100 and 200 corridors to the corner of 600 and 500 without traveling on either the 200 or 600 corridors. This would be done by traveling south on the 100 to the 400, east on the 400 to the 500 and south on the 500 to the 600.

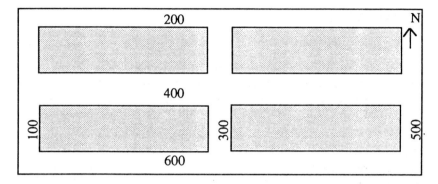

Figure 6.1: Model Environment for Indoor Travel Patterns

These patterns are developed by traveling to intersections as illustrated and/or specific objectives using the numbering system. The more complicated patterns may be developed as the student travels to a series of objectives (e.g., find rooms 408, 512, and 619). The patterns can vary depending on the order in which the objectives are located.

RESIDENTIAL ENVIRONMENTS

The student is first introduced to outdoor travel in a quiet residential environment. Initially, the student is faced with

   (a)   the problem of the cane sticking while traveling,
   (b)   maintaining a straight line without walls to define the area,
   (c)   the identification of intersecting streets, and
   (d)   crossing streets.

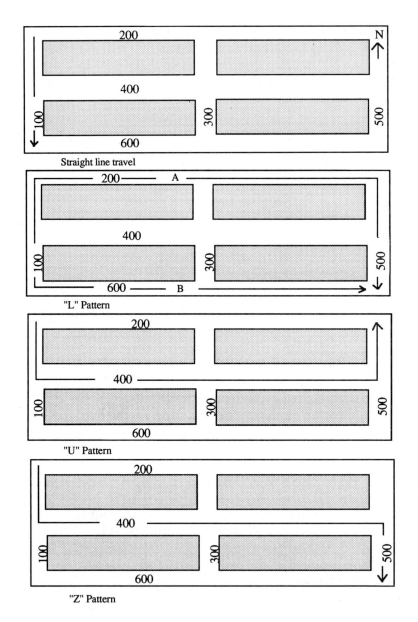

Figure 6.2: Travel Patterns Within the Model Environment

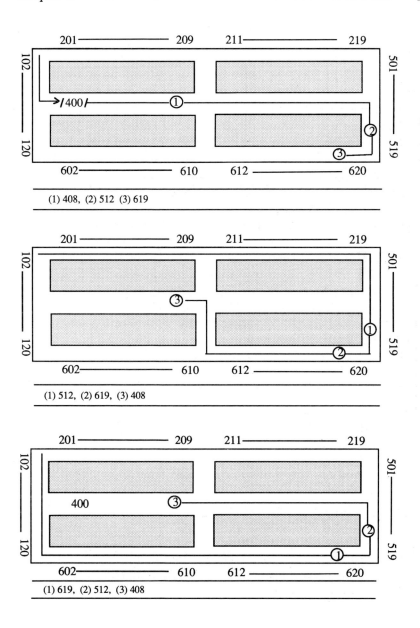

**Figure 6.3: Patterns can Vary Depending on the Order in which
the Objectives are Located**

The residential environment should have some distinctive boundaries to keep the student from traveling outside of it. It is often helpful to have at least one busy street as a boundary. Boundary streets may also be delineated by dead-ends, terrain changes (e.g., street at the bottom or top of a hill), or textural changes (e.g., a cobblestone or gravel road rather than pavement which exists everywhere else in the environment). Most streets within this environment should be lightly traveled. Students are generally cautious when crossing streets initially and like to be able to begin with no traffic present. Most intersections should be clearly defined by curbs, allowing them to be easily detected with the long cane. In many communities well-defined curbs are becoming more scarce as more and more blended curbs or curb-cuts are being built. This produces some early uncertainty for the traveler and makes difficult a built-in conditioned response to the drop-off.

A given intersection should be designated as home-base. Often this intersection is located at the juncture of two boundary streets and is selected as the quietest of the intersections along the border. If a quiet intersection does not exist along the boundaries, the home-base is located elsewhere.

Travel Patterns

Travel initially begins with a straight-line route from the home-base. The student is asked to travel to the next intersection within the given area and locate the intersection. Return trips are used to allow the student sufficient time to get used to

(a)   using the cane outdoors,
(b)   dealing with sticking,
(c)   reacting to grass-lines,
(d)   gaining confidence with the location of curbs, and
(e)   developing a kinesthetic awareness of the length of the block.

Students will often veer from the sidewalk onto the grass-line without immediately recognizing the change in texture. When this happens, the student stops and checks both sides with a sweep of the cane. If the sidewalk is not located while checking, the student turns and walks toward the parallel street. If the street is located before the sidewalk is intersected, the student turns and puts his back to the parallel street and travels in a straight line in search of the sidewalk. The upper-hand-and-forearm technique should be used in conjunction with the long cane in uncontrolled situations (e.g., when travelling over the grass strip between the street and the sidewalk).

Recovery from Driveways or Sidewalks after Veering

Similarly, the traveler may veer into an intersecting driveway or sidewalk. When this occurs, the student should:

1. Step up to the perpendicular surface contacted and continue facing the intended line of travel.

2. Initiate a three-point check with the cane; in front, 45 degrees left, and 45 degrees right.

3. If the sidewalk is not located, the traveler turns toward the parallel street and trails the contacted surface until the sidewalk is intercepted.

4. If the street is located rather than the intersecting sidewalk, the student would turn 180 degrees placing the street at his back and trail until the sidewalk is intercepted.

Once the sidewalk has been located, the traveler is required to turn and continue traveling in the intended direction. He must remain aware of the direction of intended travel and the location of the parallel street he is traveling along. This information is relevant regardless of the direction he is facing. At this point, the student is introduced to the concept of directional corners. Directional corners are also used to allow the instructor to specify the exact corner to be traveled to within an intersection.

Directional Corners

There are four corners at any standard intersection:

(a)   the northeast
(b)   the northwest
(c)   the southeast, and
(d)   the southwest.

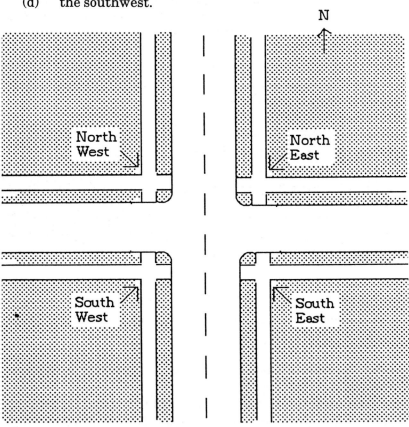

Figure 6.4: Directional Corners

The use of specific directional corners with given intersection names tells the student whether a street needs to be crossed or not. For example, if the student is told to travel from the southwest corner of Third Avenue and 1st Street to either the southeast corner of 1st Street and Second Avenue, or the northwest corner of Third Avenue and 2nd Street, the student should know that this can be done without having to cross the street. Therefore straight-line, 'L', 'U', and even rectangular patterns may be traveled before street crossings are introduced, as long as the student is kept to the confines of the block.

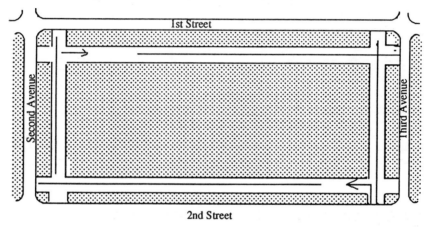

Figure 6.5: Straight line, 'L', 'U', and even rectangular patterns may be traveled before street crossings are introduced.

Expanding the Environment with 'L' and 'U' Patterns

'L' and 'U' patterns are often used to allow the student to become comfortable with trailing in outdoor environments before street crossings are introduced. These patterns provide the student with ample opportunity to locate intersecting streets and practise trailing, as each of these moves requires the student to travel to' the intersection, locate the curb, turn 180 degrees, and trail the grass-line until the intersecting sidewalk is located.

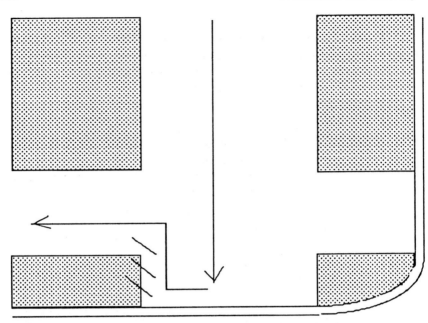

Figure 6.6: Each turn requires a 180° turn followed by a 90° turn. The inside edge is trailed to locate the intersecting sidewalk.

Repetition is important since travelers must have confidence in their trailing technique. Intersecting sidewalks are often so narrow they may be contacted only once within a stride. Therefore, any textural change encountered when trailing must be checked.

Trailing, using a two-point touch technique, is somewhat difficult in outdoor environments, initially. The student trails the grass-line maintaining the cement sidewalk underfoot and the grass to the side being trailed. This textural difference must be recognized haptically (i.e., through active exploration) and tactually (i.e., through passive recognition). Furthermore, there is often no vertical dimension in outdoor trailing to keep the traveler from moving on to the trailing surface, as there is in the indoor environment. The tip also tends to stick in the grass as one attempts to trail it. Despite this, the student must learn to maintain his position on the sidewalk near the grass-line by keeping the cane centered and the arc at its proper width while responding to all textural changes experienced immediately.

Once street crossings are introduced, the instructor can control the difficulty of the street crossing by determining whether it is preceded by

(a) a straight line (e.g., from the southwest corner of 1st Street and Third Avenue to the Southwest Corner of 2nd Street and Third Avenue),

(b) a 90-degree turn (e.g., to the southeast corner of 2nd Street and Third Avenue), or

(c) a series of turns (e.g., to the northeast corner of 2nd Street and Third Avenue).

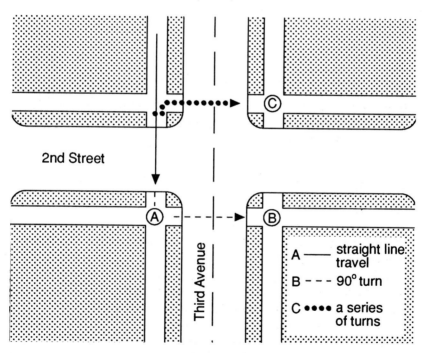

Figure 6.7: The difficulty of the crossing may be determined by the demands preceeding it.

The instructor may use extended 'L' patterns to introduce the student to the entire area. The student is usually introduced to one of the boundary streets first and all of the intersecting streets by travelling the first leg of the 'L' pattern (e.g., travel from the southwest corner of 1st Street and Third Avenue to the northwest corner of 3rd Street and Third Avenue), and then the rest of the grid by completing the 'L' pattern (e.g., travel from the northwest corner of 1st Street and Third Avenue to the northeast corner of 3rd Street and First Avenue). None of this can be accomplished until street crossings are mastered, however.

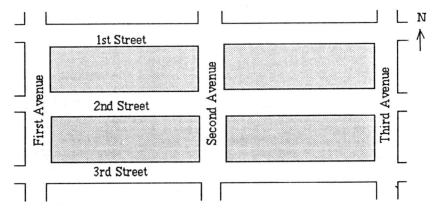

Figure 6.8: Model Residential Environment

Street Crossings, Methods of Alignment and Recovery Techniques

Street crossings are initially taught when there is an absence of traffic on both the perpendicular and parallel street.

Once the curb is located the student establishes alignment with the parallel street using one or more of the following methods of alignment:

Methods of Alignment

Objective

To provide the traveler with methods of aligning the body in a parallel relationship to the street in order to facilitate straight-line crossings.

Procedure: Parallel Alignment with Grass-line

1. The student locates the grass-line farthest from the parallel street and sidesteps to it.

2. The student uses the foot to establish a parallel direction with the grass-line.

3. The rest of the body is then positioned accordingly.

Procedure: Perpendicular Alignment with Curb

1. The student has *prior knowledge* that the curb is square (making this determination with the cane is nearly impossible).

2. The toes are extended over the curb in order to feel the curb's edge under foot (rolling the weight forward may help).

3. Having established perpendicular alignment, the traveler projects this line into space.

Procedure: **Maintaining Line of Direction**

1. The traveler acquires a straight line and carries this line to the curb.

2. The traveler mentally projects this acquired line across the street. This assumes an *actual* mental process.

Procedure: **Auditory Parallel or Perpendicular Alignment with Traffic Sounds**

1. Having located the curb, the traveler maintains his line of travel.

2. The traveler aligns his body in relation to the available traffic sounds.

    (a)   Parallel alignment requires tracking individual cars into the distance and aligning the body accordingly.
    (b)   Perpendicular alignments requires the traveler to square his shoulders to the traffic at its loudest point.

3. The traveler now mentally projects the intended line of travel.

The use of the grass-line and square curb methods are considered basic techniques. In general, once a student establishes some consistency with straight-line travel in the block preceeding the crossing, the method of choice becomes that of maintaining a line of direction with verification from parallel traffic sounds (Hill & Ponder, 1976; Guth, Hill & Rieser, 1989). This may occur very early in the residential experience. The use of parallel traffic sounds is emphasized as soon as possible. However, sufficient traffic for this procedure is not usually present until the traveler has moved on to a busier environment.

Crossing Streets

Objective

To provide the traveler with a safe and efficient method for crossing quiet residential streets.

Procedure

1. Upon detection of the curb, the cane is anchored there and brought to a vertical position. The student steps up to the cane and positions himself at the curb.

2. The area immediately in front of the traveler is cleared with a sweep of the cane to ensure that it is safe to step out into this space and that the intersection had indeed been located.

3. When waiting to cross the street, the traveler holds the cane diagonally across his body. Care should be taken to ensure that it is extended far enough to the side to be visible to drivers approaching the traveler from the rear.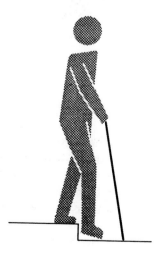

4. The traveler initiates the crossing when

    (a) there is no traffic approaching from either the parallel or perpendicular street, or

(b)   there is traffic on the parallel street, but it is deemed to be moving too fast to turn on to the perpendicular street and thus into the intended path of travel.

5. The traveler re-establishes his alignment before stepping off the curb to cross the street.

6. When crossing the street, the traveler mentally projects a straight line, shifts his weight forward, takes a dominant first step and crosses the street at a fairly rapid pace.

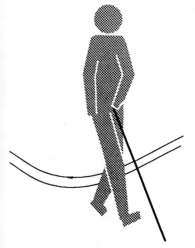

7. When the curb at the opposite end of the street is located, the traveler steps forward to the curb as he brings his cane up to a vertical position, then checks the surface (using a three-point check) above the curb for the continuing sidewalk.
   If the sidewalk is located, the traveler steps up and continues on his way. If it is not, the traveler assumes a veer has occurred.

Recovering from Veers

The traveler may veer into the perpendicular street or the parallel street. The traveler usually becomes aware of a veer into the perpendicular street after checking above the curb to find the sidewalk. If the sidewalk is not located following the three-point check, the traveler assumes a veer into the perpendicular street has occurred. In this case, the traveler would turn to face the parallel street, align himself beside the curb and begin trailing using a three-point technique in an attempt to locate the sidewalk (Hill & Ponder, 1976).

The student needs to be aware of his position in relation to the parallel street at all times. For example, if the student is traveling south from the northwest corner to the southwest corner, one should be aware that the parallel street is to the east and is therefore to the left. Any response to an inside veer should be initiated by turning to the left.

The three-point trailing technique may be introduced just before street crossings are taught. Instructors will often simulate veers using human guide or have the student purposefully line up to the inside of the intersection during initial crossings to ensure that a veer to the inside occurs. Students should have ample opportunity to practise this awkward technique as it needs to be used with confidence when an actual veer does occur.

Veers into the parallel street are usually recognized kinesthetically; travelers simply feel that they have traveled too far for a standard street crossing. They may also note that the expected incline/decline of the camber is replaced with a lateral tilt or a prolonged leveling of the surface traveled. In this case, the student turns away from the parallel street (e.g., to the right in the example above) and moves rapidly out of the street. The student learns to turn approximately 100 degrees when making this move. This is done to minimize the time in the street and cut the distance to be traveled to return to the curb. Once the curb has been located, the traveler turns back toward the intersection or steps up into the grass verge and moves across it to find the sidewalk using an upper-hand-and-forearm technique to protect the upper body in this uncontrolled environment. The decision made is in accordance with the traveler's intended route after the street crossing.

The instructor needs to be aware of the direction of veers. If the student is consistently veering in one direction regardless of the location of the parallel street, it is probably due to an alignment or stylistic problem. However, if the veer is consistently away from or toward the parallel street regardless of the side that street is on, it is probably attributable to psychological rather than technical factors.

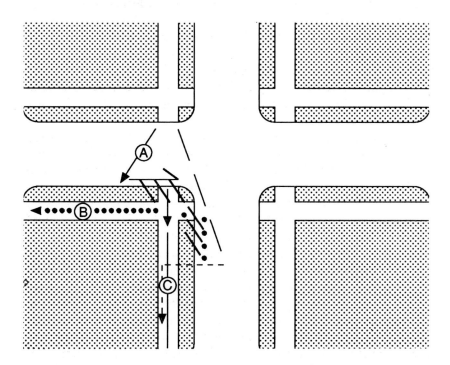

Figure 6.9: **When veering into the perpendicular street, the traveler (A) turns to the parallel street and trails to find the intersecting street. When veering into the parallel street, the traveler turns 100° away from the parallel street and goes to the curb. At this point he either turns toward the perpendicular street and trails to find the intersecting sidewalk (B), or steps up across the median (C) and continues on his way.**

Locating Specific Objectives

The objectives to be located within residential areas are typically specified by house number. As a result, the location of specific objectives is used to introduce the student to the outdoor numbering system, reinforce the rules of the numbering system, identify exceptions to the rule, give the student the opportunity to solicit information concerning location, clue and landmark, and provide the student with practice trailing. This process is also used to provide the student with ample opportunity to plan his own route of travel.

Numbering systems vary from place to place. However, they all work upon a set of rules. They often correspond to grid patterns and emanate from the city center. Typically, numbers begin at a focal point and increase outward in all four directions. As a result, there may be a 403 South Park and a 403 North Park, as well as a 403 East College and a 403 West College. The first digit of a number often corresponds to the number of blocks it is from the focal point. For example, 403 South Park may be located in the fourth block south of the focal point. Similarly 1403 South Park would be ten blocks further south. In this system, the numbers would start again at each intersection (i.e., blocks may be numbered from 101, 201, 301, etc.). The ending numbers would depend upon the length of the block and the position of the last house within the block. In this case, the plots are numbered rather than the buildings. As a result, you may find that 305 and 323 are the only two houses on a street within the block. Or the numbering system may emanate in only two directions, from a municipal boundary or a natural feature in the environment (e.g., river). The actual houses may be numbered rather than the plots, or the house number may indicate the actual number of houses or plots a location is from a focal point. Numbers may run up one side of a street and back down the other with no odd-even correspondence. It is up to the instructor to identify these patterns and convey them to the student.

At times, exceptions to the rule exist. For example, 401 North Park could be located in the middle of the block, following 325. If this was the case, it would be likely that the number split (i.e., from 300 to 400) corresponded to an intersecting street which affected the numbering system but was not present in this particular neighborhood (e.g., it may not continue through the grid due to the presence of a school, hospital or park, which interrupts the pattern). In this case, the block would be likely to be twice as long as most other blocks in the area.

The odd and even designation usually indicate the side of the street (e.g., odd numbers on the north and west, evens on the south and east) the house is located on. Given this information then, we would guess that 303 North Park was probably located near the northwest corner of Park and the third street north (i.e., Third Street in this example) of the focal point. We would also suspect that 223 North Park was near the southwest corner of that intersection, given that the average length of a block didn't exceed 25. We would not necessarily know if either of these addresses were the first or second from the corner, however.

Once the rules are known, a number of assumptions can be made by knowing the house number of the objective. However, everything needed to pinpoint a location is not contained within its address. As a result, the traveler often needs additional clues or landmark information.

The student is often required to gain locational information from the instructor. Once this information is gained, it is usually organized in relation to the nearest directional corner. The student is then given the opportunity to plan his route from his present location to the specific directional corner identified.

For example, we may find that 221 North Park is the third house (third sidewalk) on Park from the southwest corner of North Park and West Third Street. Therefore, the student would travel to the southwest corner of North Park and West Third and then begin trailing south on the west side of North Park until the third sidewalk after the intersection is located (the footpath running parallel to Third is not counted).

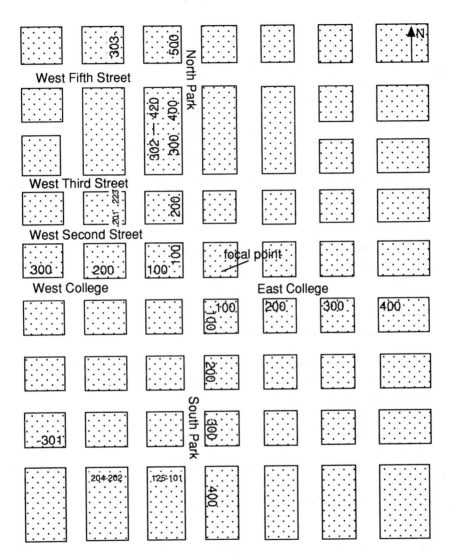

Figure 6.10:   Model City Numbering System

The same strategy would apply no matter where the student was coming from (i.e., travel to the nearest directional corner to the objective and then trail to the specific location) as long as the objective was near a corner. When locating a mid-block location other strategies may be employed, including the location of alleys or other landmarks or clues.

BUSINESS ENVIRONMENTS

Business environments, including the transitional semi-business area, pose a number of new challenges to the traveler. These environments require the traveler to

(a)　travel along sidewalks which are continuous from building line to curb,
(b)　deal with busy, complex environments,
(c)　cross busy, traffic light-controlled intersections, and
(d)　locate stores and objectives which are not simply identified by locating intersecting sidewalks.

Sidewalks in residential environments are often fairly narrow and are typically delineated by grass on either side. As a result, it is relatively easy to maintain a straight line of travel in this environment. Any deviation from a straight line is quickly discovered. This is not the case in business environments. In these environments, the paved sidewalk typically extends from building line to curb. The area is quite wide. The traveler may not be aware of any deviation from the intended line of travel until discovering a curb on one side, or a building on the other. Parking lots and driveways may blend into the paved environment, providing little or no textural indication that the traveler has left the sidewalk.

The traveler must become more attuned auditorially as well as proprioceptively (i.e., aware of inclines, declines and lateral tilts). The sidewalk if often slanted toward the street near the curb. The traveler should be aware of this occurrence and react to lateral tilts by stepping back up on the sidewalk away from the parallel street. If the curb is detected instead, the student may wish to turn his back to the parallel street and ascend the incline (i.e., now perpendicular to tilt), turning back to continue on his way when the flat of the sidewalk is relocated, or simply estimate the distance (3-4 steps).

The area between the intended path of travel and the curb often contains signs, parking meters, trash receptacles, light poles, bike stands and other obstacles to safe travel. The traveler should move out of this area as soon as it is recognized.

The student should also be aware of the traffic flow on the parallel street and attempt to maintain a steady distance from it. Traffic sound may also be trailed auditorially. The traveler may use this information to maintain a straight line, or re-establish one if necessary. Building lines may also be trailed auditorially using the sound generated by traffic on the parallel street. The traveler may maintain a steady distance from the building line or identify breaks in the building line by noticing a change in the reflected sound, or a difference in air currents.

Pedestrians may also provide a clue to the location of the intended path of travel in these environments. The traveler will often tune into the general flow of pedestrians. However, one must be aware that any given pedestrian or group of pedestrians can deviate from the path, jay walk, walk against the light, and/ or take unacceptable risks while traveling. Therefore, the traveler must use this information selectively as with all other sensory input.

Students are often intimidated by busy streets when first encountering them. However, the traveler soon finds that a wealth of information is provided by high traffic volume. Experienced travelers often plan their route of travel along busy streets, avoiding quiet ones.

Travel Patterns

Travel usually starts with straight-line runs. The student begins by crossing quiet intersecting streets while traveling parallel with a busy roadway. The student will work along one side of the street learning to deal with the open walkways and locate objectives in a semi-business environment. Crossing at light-controlled intersections is introduced before the student is expected to travel to and find objectives on both sides of the busy street.

Travel in semi-business environments is often limited to straight-line travel with crossings from one side of the street to the other. Once the transition is made from narrow to wide sidewalks, quiet to busy streets, and uncontrolled to controlled intersections, the student moves on into the business environment.

Students are typically introduced to business environments using straight-line runs from along a boundary street. In this way all intersecting streets are met and named. 'L' patterns are then used to have the student travel to specified corners or objectives located on corners. 'U', 'Z' and rectangle patterns are used to introduce the student to the entire environment while pointing out landmarks and major clues within the area. Mid-block objectives are then introduced as is the use of multiple-objective runs.

Structured solicitation is used in earnest in this environment to allow the student the opportunity to gain locational information independently. The student uses this information to plan the run from the starting point to the objective.

The home base is often moved from the periphery of the area to a bus stop within the business district prior to introducing bus travel. As a result, the bus stop becomes a comfortable home base for the student when he begins to travel to the business district independently by this means.

Street Crossing and Recovery in the Business Environment

The traveler is usually limited to crossing busy streets at light-controlled intersections. In this way, the traveler crosses with the parallel traffic ensuring that traffic cannot be moving through the street being crossed. The traveler should always cross at the beginning of the light to ensure that the traffic is moving from a dead stop, and thus must actively accelerate to move into his path of travel if turning. If the traffic surge (i.e., sound of two or more cars starting up and moving through the intersection from a complete stop) is missed, or if a clear surge is not present, the traveler must wait through the cycle. Prior to being introduced to traffic lights, the traveler has been sequentially exposed to a variety of traffic sounds with increasing volume. The prerequisite skills of auditory alignment will need to be fairly well developed before introducing the traffic light as well.

The traveler approaches the intersection, stops and listens to the traffic to determine if the intersection is controlled by a traffic control device. Cars individually stopping, waiting then moving through the intersection are usually responding to a stop, yield or give-way sign. Traffic which collectively flows through the intersection, or stops and waits is probably responding to a traffic control device. The traveler must listen to a cycle to determine the pattern. The traffic on a given street may all be released at once or there may be arrows controlling turning traffic. At times the cycle also includes a time for pedestrians to cross when all other traffic is stopped. This may be indicated by a buzzer or other audible signal (Hill & Ponder, 1976).

Traffic Light Crossings

Objective

To safely and efficiently cross at traffic light-controlled intersections.

Procedure

1. Upon detection of the perpendicular street or curb, the traveler stops and anchors the cane against the curb in a diagonal position

with cane visible to the side of parallel traffic.

2. Initially, the traveler may wait through one light cycle to determine the sequence of traffic and to establish parallel alignment.

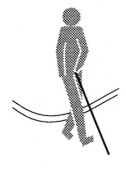

3. The traveler initiates the crossing when there is a surge of parallel movement. The initiation of the crossing may be delayed until the traffic breaks the plane of the center of the intersection to ensure that cars are not simply turning right on a red light where permissible.

4. The street is crossed with a quickened pace and the traveler continues to monitor the traffic for alignment.

5. As the opposite curb is reached the traveler clears with the cane and continues.

Experienced travelers often will not wait through one light cycle and in fact should be encouraged to cross on the initial surge. If one intersecting street is considerably busier than the other, the busier street will have a longer green light. This has implications for the amount of recovery time available should a veer occur.

The business environment can provide confusing or masking sounds at times and the traveler should not attempt the crossing under these conditions. Alternative measures include: soliciting assistance, altering the route, or waiting until the conflicting sounds diminish. Patterns of traffic are sometimes altered by emergency vehicles, funeral processions, buses or road construction crews.

The instructor needs to monitor from an appropriate position at busy intersections. This is accomplished by standing behind and slightly to the side of the student, at a 45-degree angle to the intersection. This position allows a good view of the traveler and the intersection with its corresponding traffic flow, and does not interfere with the immediate environment of the traveler.

Identifying the surge and initiating the crossing in a timely matter is important. The traveler should indicate a readiness to begin the crossing by stepping up to the curb, clearing with the cane, bringing it back to the starting position, pausing briefly then stepping out. Lurching forward in an exaggerated step is not recommended as it may be difficult for the traveler to stop if a car is turning in front of him. Sometimes the exaggerated step is used in residential crossings to facilitate a straight line. This, however, is not appropriate here.

Without a surge it is difficult for a traveler to determine exactly where he is within the cycle. At any time other than the beginning of a cycle, he may find cars turning into the path of travel at fairly high rates. If crossing at the end of the cycle, he may be faced with moving cars accelerating to beat the beginning of the light in the perpendicular street.

The mechanics of crossing busy light-controlled intersections are the same as that used for crossing quiet residential streets, except that the traveler may use the heavier parallel traffic to establish a line for crossing or to correct the line while crossing (Hill & Ponder, 1976). The recovery technique is somewhat different however. Typically, the traveler will respond to any veer by moving off the street first, and then moving to the sidewalk to recover the line of travel. In this way, time on the street is minimized.

Street crossings at busy intersections are typically introduced to the student by having him cross quieter sign-controlled perpendicular streets while traveling along a busy parallel street. In this way, the student can take advantage of busy parallel traffic to establish and maintain his line without having to worry about the traffic in the perpendicular street.

When the student is introduced to light-controlled intersections, he often begins by crossing a one-way street. In some cases the human guide technique may be used for initial attempts until confidence is gained. Crossing at one-way streets allows the instructor to control the situation so that no traffic will turn into the perpendicular street during the crossing, as in the case of crossing from the northwest to the southwest corner in the illustration below.

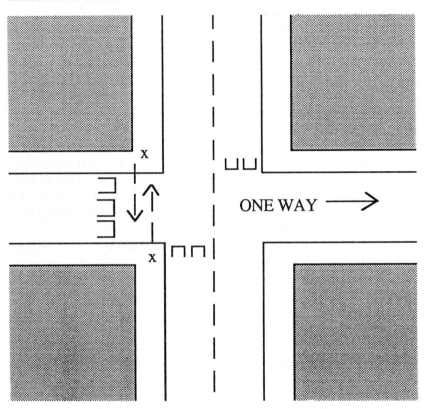

Figure 6.11: Crossing a one-way street to ensure that cars cannot turn into the path of travel.

As skill is gained, the student will continue with this intersection, crossing it from the other side of the street, then with the one-way street (i.e., from the n.w. to n.e. corner or the s.w. to the s.e.) and then against it. Crossing with the parallel flow is easier than crossing against it. The student would then move on to light-controlled intersections with arrows, offset intersections, intersections with pedestrian islands, and other more complex crossings.

Locating Specific Objectives

Locating objectives within business environments is somewhat more complex a task than that experienced in the residential environment. The objective is located in relation to a directional corner and clues and/or landmarks are used to specify its exact location, as was previously done in both the residential and indoor environments. However, the clues used are far more varied, and often more subtle than those available in other environments. As a result, the traveler must be quite consistent when trailing and precise in his movements. A fair amount of experience is required for the traveler to gain confidence in this. The entire business environment may be introduced and all lessons planned around the location of specific objectives. Students are often expected to gain the locational information needed through phone or pedestrian solicitation. The routes are often planned by the student, as is the exact approach to finding the objective. Objectives (destinations) are selected according to the intrinsic orientation (e.g. a landmark or dominant clue) or mobility value (e.g., the presence of escalators) they may provide, or the interest and/or need of the student.

7

Special Travel Environments

During the course of a complete orientation and mobility program, the instructor will introduce the student to a number of special travel environments. These typically include shopping malls, department stores, supermarkets, rural areas and railroad crossings. In each, principles of travel which are transferable across environments are taught to promote generalization and therefore minimize the need for specific instruction in each new or different environment encountered.

SURBURBAN SHOPPING MALLS

Prior to the 1960s, retail centers were generally located in downtown business districts. Today, however, many retailers have moved to the suburbs. They are increasingly located in clusters along major arteries either in covered shopping malls or plazas.

The shopping mall is by far the most popular, offering the shopper a weather-free, temperature-controlled environment. They are typically anchored by at least one major department store and many are multi-floored with both elevators and escalators for access.

The shopping mall is a unique environment posing a number of special considerations for travelers who are visually impaired.

Travel Considerations

Objective

To provide methods of travel which will ensure safety in congested pedestrian environments and minimize cane contact with pedestrians.

Procedure

1. The traveler assumes a position to the side of the aisle, approximately a cane's length from the building line.

2. The conventional technique is modified so that

   (a)   the arc width does not exceed the shoulders,
   (b)   the cane is in a less forward position, and
   (c)   the constant-contact technique is employed.

3. The traveler proceeds, mentally projecting to a forward point while adapting his pace to the amount of pedestrian traffic encountered.

   Projecting to a forward point of general orientation is essential, (e.g. going toward the department store) to maintain a line of travel in this rather featureless travel environment.

Sequencing Considerations

Initially lessons should be located at a one-level, symmetrically designed mall to ensure safety and enhance orientation. The instructor may begin with a familiarization to the overall layout, including landmarks and other information points. Routes would then include:

(a) traveling end-to-end to build the 'whole' concept,
(b) locating specific major objectives,
(c) solicitation to find secondary objectives, and
(d) eventual travel throughout the entire mall.

The instructor may include the use of tactual and auditory mapping in this environment. Eventually lessons would progress to include negotiating the interior of large department stores, with their escalators, elevators, and revolving doors.

DEPARTMENT STORES

Department stores, whether located in shopping malls or downtown areas, are usually selected as destinations because of their value as a travel environment, interest to the learner or accessible location. Having selected a particular store, the instructor may choose to ask permission to use it as a training site. However, aware that she may be denied permission due to liability issues in some places, she may simply begin to use the store for training purposes taking the opportunity to educate the affected personnel as the need arises. Care should be exercised not to interfere with normal operations of the store or pedestrian traffic within it. Certain instructional areas (e.g. escalators), might best be presented during times the store is less busy. Given a few common courtesies, store owners and managers will usually be most cooperative.

The same considerations would apply to travel within the department store as applied to travel in the mall. Speed of travel (pace) however might need to be slower to avoid undue contact. The following general principles may apply to the layout of department stores:

(a)   Major aisles run directly to and from the main entrances.

(b)   Store aisles often run parallel and perpendicular to the outside walls.

(c)   Elevators are most often located on inside walls.

(d)   Escalators are usually found toward the center of the store adjacent to a main aisle.

(e)   Carpet or rubber matting is often located immediately in front of the door.

In general, the traveler should avoid unnecessary tactual exploration, but when essential, do so carefully and efficiently. When traveling the aisles the student should avoid hugging the counters as a loose coat or shoulder bag may brush merchandise off the counters.

Once some level of proficiency is achieved, travel throughout the entire store is made possible using escalators and elevators. Escalators may be the conveyance of choice if travel between two to five floors is desired. Typically, escalators do not go beyond the 5th or 6th level. It is also easier for the student to maintain orientation on the escalator. However, elevators are faster, and of course necessary for negotiating tall buildings.

Escalators

Objective

To enable the traveler to locate and use the escalator in a safe, efficient and independent manner.

Procedure

1. The traveler approaches the escalator using the touch-and-slide or the constant-contact technique.

2. The traveler is alert for sound clues and/or the metal plate often located directly in front of the escalator. Soliciting assistance to locate the escalator may be necessary.

3. The traveler locates the handrail with the free hand to determine if the escalator is moving away from him and is thus boardable.

4. The traveler then moves forward to the edge of the metal grate and extends the cane forward with the tip resting on the moving escalator to determine if the escalator is moving up or down.

   In ascending, the cane tip will raise slightly and then drop off the emerging steps. In descending, the cane tip is moved forward slightly and then back as each emerging step pushes against the tip.

5. The traveler steps on to the escalator, grasps the handrail, and adjusts his feet accordingly.

6. The traveler should place one foot slightly forward on the step with his weight over the back foot. The cane may be vertical with the tip resting one step forward to aid in detecting the landing.

7. As the handrail and the stairs level off, the toe of the forward foot is raised slightly and allowed to contact the landing.

8. As the traveler steps off the escalator, it is necessary to move directly ahead with good technique to avoid congestion from behind.

Escalators moving to and from the main floor are often wider than those on succeeding floors. Escalators traveling in the same direction (up) are generally located side by side. The traveler would need to turn 180 degrees after leaving one to board the next. Escalators moving in opposite directions are usually located behind each other. Patterns may differ in individual stores.

When a human guide is being used it is often necessary for her to break contact and have the traveler precede the guide as there is not room for both on the stairs.

Elevators

Objective

To provide the traveler with a safe and efficient method of independently using an elevator.

Procedure

1. The traveler locates the elevator, alert to auditory clues such as a bell, an opening door, or pedestrian footsteps. Solicitation may be necessary.

2. After pressing the call button, which is usually located on the wall at waist height

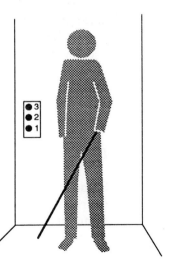

between or near the elevator door, the traveler steps back and takes position to have access to the first elevator available.

3. When the elevator arrives, the traveler pauses briefly, then enters with a short-ened-cane technique. If the elevator door begins to close during entrance, he should employ a modified upper-hand-and-forearm technique to contact the bumper which automatically retracts the door.

4. The traveler turns and faces the door and locates the button panel or asks for the desired floor to be pushed.

5. When the floor is reached, the traveler verifies his location and exits with a modified (shortened) cane technique.

If a particular elevator is used frequently, the traveler should become familiar with the selection panel. In general, travel is made easier if the traveler is assertive and expediently uses pedestrians. Many elevators now have braille markers to assist users who are blind. Floor markers are located on the inside of the metal door frame and braille is also located adjacent to the button panel inside the elevator (Wiener, 1992). Some elevators have intercom systems announcing the floors. With practice, a traveler may use an elevator very efficiently.

Revolving Doors

Some department stores, banks/or public buildings have revolving doors. After a few trials the blind traveler usually has no difficulty managing these. Conventional doors are generally located nearby for those who cannot manage a revolving door.

Objective

To provide the traveler with a safe and efficient method of independently using a revolving door.

Procedure

1. The traveler approaches the door from the right side to avoid congestion at the entrance.

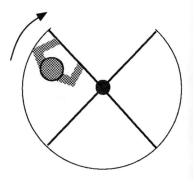

2. The traveler tactually identifies the door or locates it by trailing the building line, alert to sound cues from the door. Some revolving doors will protrude out from the building line and be encased in a cylinder.

3. When the door is reached, the traveler uses the upper-hand-and-forearm with the left hand, holding the cane in the right.

4. The traveler makes a right turn behind the upper-hand-and-forearm, contacting the edge of the door.

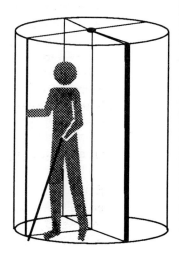

5. If the door is moving, the traveler can time his entrance into the cylinder by moving in directly behind the flaps of the door that brush the heel of the hand.

6. The cane is held in a semi-diagonal position close to the body.

7. The traveler lightly trails the inside wall with the right elbow until it ends. He

should also be alert for thermal or auditory changes indicating the point of exit.

8. The traveler exits quickly, turning slightly to the right to re-establish his intended line and avoid contacting people entering from the opposite side.

9. As the exit is made, the traveler resumes the use of the standard touch technique.

When using a human guide it will be necessary to break contact and have the blind traveler enter the doors ahead or behind of the guide in his own individual quandrant as there is not space for two adults in one section.

SUPERMARKETS

People generally utilize supermarkets in two ways: to buy food and household items for a week or so, or to pick up a few items. Buying larger quantities of goods requires some forward planning, especially if assistance from store personnel is expected. Planning the trip to coincide with a slow time in the store and organizing the shopping list to reflect the general layout of the store will help to maintain the goodwill of those providing the assistance. The mobility instructor can facilitate this, if necessary, by arranging a meeting between the traveler and the store manager for the purpose of introducing the two and identifying the various needs of each. Additionally, the traveler must arrange some way to get the groceries home. Options include the use of taxis, community transport and volunteer services.

The traveler may also drop into the supermarket at any time to pick up a few items and this can be handled independently in most cases. Supermarkets are generally laid out so that most immediate need items are located along the outside edge of the store. Typically, fruits and vegetables, dairy products, meats and breads are located on the outside aisles, as are the bakery, deli, butchery and other specialty areas of the store. As a result the traveler can access most things that he would need by entering the store and traveling along the perimeter without ever entering the middle aisles. In addition, help with selection can be obtained from the various speciality counters which are normally manned. Thus, we find that larger supermarkets tend to provide a more personal and accessible service than normally found in smaller grocery stores.

Objective

To provide a safe and efficient method for independently shopping in supermarkets to meet immediate needs.

Procedure

1. The traveler enters the market and moves to the outside aisle with the intent of moving around the perimeter of the store using a modified touch and slide or constant-contact technique.

2. As each section of the store is encountered (e.g., fruit and vegetables, dairy, cold meats, bread racks, etc.), the traveler either moves along its length to identify the particular items desired, or moves to the counter if it is manned, to gain assistance, (e.g., deli, fish shop, bakery, butchery).

3. Upon completing the circuit, the traveler moves toward the check-out counters, being alert for queues and other indications of an open counter.

Teaching Considerations

These procedures are usually introduced to the student by

(a) guiding him through the store and pointing out the various counters and product groups,

(b) having the student travel the perimeter and locate each section of interest when doing so, and

(c) conducting a number of performance runs in which the student is asked to locate specified items along the route.

Performance runs are usually conducted until the student feels confident both in negotiating the store and finding various items of interest.

RURAL AREAS

The rural environment is characterized by

(a) the absence of sidewalks,

(b) poorly defined shorelines (reference lines),

(c) increased distance between perpendicular streets, and increased speed of traffic,

(d) fewer landmarks aiding orientation, and

(e) generally diminished feedback from the environment.

Some areas which are lacking in sidewalks, do have curbs however. This provides the traveler with a consistent point of reference and a relatively easy environment to negotiate. Newer residential areas frequently have curbs but no sidewalks, whereas truly rural environments have neither.

Travel Without Sidewalks

Objective

To provide the traveler with a safe method of traveling along roads or streets where no sidewalk exists.

Procedure

1. The traveler takes a position next to the parallel curb, shoreline, or edge of road.

2. Using a two-point touch or touch-and-drag technique, the traveler maintains parallel alignment with the reference point.

3. The traveler mentally projects a straight line. This will facilitate the recognition of change (curve or cessation) in the reference line.

Under most circumstances the traveler would walk the side of the roadway *against* the traffic. If the road is sufficiently wide or a bike path is present, this would not be necessary. Caution should be exercised when cresting a hill, as the traveler is obscured from the driver's view. The hill may also obstruct the sound of the approaching vehicle. Crossing the road near the hill's crest should be avoided.

Street Crossings Without Sidewalks

Objective

To provide the traveler a safe and efficient method of crossing streets in areas where no sidewalk is present.

Procedure 1

1. The traveler recognizes the perpendicular street by the curving of the reference line (shoreline) away from the parallel street.

2. The traveler follows the curving reference line until a 90-degree turn is complete.

3. The traveler places the curb or reference line to his back and squares off with the edge of the street.

4. The traveler projects a straight line and crosses the street.

or

Procedure 2

1. The traveler continues straight-line travel until the street is crossed.

2. The traveler realigns his position if necessary with the parallel reference line or curb after crossing the perpendicular street or at the time he assumes he has traveled far enough to have crossed it.

A key to successful travel in this environment is the traveler's ability to establish a straight line of travel and project that line into space. It is this emphasis which allows him to maintain his position in space. If concentration is shifted to the cane tip or the walking surface, it is possible for the traveler to round a corner completing a 90-degree turn without any knowledge that a turn has been made. It is the mental projection to an imaginary point in the distance that makes recognition of a change in the reference line possible.

If a curb lines the street, the standard two-point trailing technique works well. However, when the edge of the road is less well defined, the touch-and-drag technique may be useful. Also, when the edge of the road has good definition, an experienced or proficient traveler might contact the curb or edge intermittently rather than with every arc to that side.

RAILROAD CROSSINGS

Some visually impaired travelers, because of where they live or work, regularly encounter railroad crossings. Others who travel rather extensively and often find themselves in new environments may also encounter railroad crossings, but for many blind travelers this special environment is just not a concern. Whether it is included in the orientation and mobility sequence then, depends on the traveler's need and level of functioning.

Objective

To provide a safe and efficient method of crossing railroad tracks.

Procedure

1. The traveler approaches the railroad tracks using constant contact and is alert to the following indicators:

    (a)   predetermined landmarks,
    (b)   sound of warning bell or train whistle,
    (c)   sound of cars crossing the tracks,
    (d)   slight incline preceding the tracks,
    (e)   contact with barricade, tracks, or textured grating.

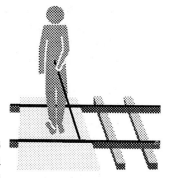

2. If a train is approaching, the traveler stops a safe distance back and waits for the train to pass. A predetermined landmark works well for this purpose.

3. If no train is present, the traveler continues the line of direction, paralleling the traffic while proceeding with the touch technique.

If the traveler has prior knowledge that the tracks are perpendicular to the intended line, squaring off on the tracks may be helpful, however paralleling traffic when available would be the method of choice.

Maintaining orientation while crossing the tracks is of utmost importance. If the tracks are frequently crossed, a familiar landmark should be sought out which gives the traveler a definite position in space in relation to the tracks. If the warning bells begin while the traveler is in the process of crossing, it is important that he stay calm and continue straight ahead at a quickened pace. If, however, the traveler has prior knowledge that multiple tracks exist and only one set has been crossed, it would be prudent to turn around and return to safe territory.

OTHER ENVIRONMENTS

Other unique travel environments may require special lessons. These might include train platforms, subways, airports, university campuses, or any number of other special situations. Special instruction may be offered to meet these unique situations or the traveler might use familiarization and solicitation skills while applying previously learned skills and methods. The ability to employ previously learned transferable skills to a new environment is perhaps the highest form of independent functioning in orientation and mobility.

8

Use of Public Transportation

Public transportation extends the range of travel for visually impaired persons as the automobile does for those who drive. Public transport can be used to travel from one city or town to another or to access various locales within a city.

TRAVEL BETWEEN CITIES

Most cities can be reached by bus, train or air. Planes tend to be the quickest means of travel between cities. However, they are also the most expensive, serve the fewest locales and are often the most difficult to access. Trains tend to be quicker than buses, but serve fewer cities. The difference in cost is often negligible. Buses tend to be the most flexible, albeit slowest, form of intercity travel.

Tickets may be purchased when departing or in advance from the train station, airport, airline office or from a travel agency. It is often convenient to arrange for the ticket by phone and have it held at the check-in desk.

All forms of public transport will offer some assistance to the blind traveler. Travelers may find it most convenient to inform the carrier of their special needs when making reservations.

Airlines are especially good at providing assistance with check-in, boarding, deplaning, and locating connecting flights or ground transport. Train and bus lines generally provide less comprehensive services. Travelers may have to make specific arrangements for sighted assistance to negotiate large, noisy bus or train depots, locate ticket booths, information booths, and the particular bus or train to be boarded. Assistance is usually available from the driver of the bus or others at the terminal for boarding, locating luggage when disembarking, and finding a phone, cab or connecting bus stop. Trains, on the other hand, pose special problems for the visually impaired traveler, especially a commuter train to an unfamiliar station.

'Disembarking from commuter trains can cause problems since the doors may open only half way, fail to open, or close before the traveler reaches them. In some cases the door may open when the train has come to a stop but is not at a platform. An additional problem is the variable width of the gap between the train and the platform. There is no way of predicting this width in an unfamiliar station. After getting off the train, the traveler may not know if he is on a single or double-track platform, which direction he should walk to exit the station, and/or where phones are located for calling a cab. In some cases the traveler may actually have to walk in front of the train to leave the station. As a result, sighted assistance is almost always necessary. Yet, small suburban railroad stations may be deserted. Frequently, ticket offices are closed except during commuter rush hours' (Eames & Eames, 1990, p. 24).

Accessing the City from the Station

Travel objectives within a town or city may be accessed from the airport, station or depot by taxi, train or bus. Commuter trains are often located within the same station as intercity trains. Taxis are typically available when trains, intercity buses and planes arrive. If not, they may be called. Airport shuttles are usually available in the bigger airports. Shuttles will often serve a more limited number of stops than a taxi, but will cost less. Some hotels/motels provide an airport limo or free pick-up service.

TRAVEL WITHIN CITIES

Taxis, buses and trains may be available for travel within cities. Taxis are generally the quickest and most convenient of the alternatives. Unfortunately, they are also the most expensive. They may be relied upon to pick the traveler up and drop him at his destination. When calling the taxi, travelers are typically expected to state their present location, identify the destination of travel, and indicate the time the taxi is required.

A number of other services are available to disabled persons, such as 'Dial-A-Ride' and 'Total Mobility'. These schemes may use their own vehicles or purchase the service from a commercial carrier. This service may be available free to the traveler or at a substantially reduced cost. However, these systems may be less convenient than taxis as they often require substantial (i.e., up to 24 hours) forward notice.

Buses and trains are generally a less convenient means of travel, but are usually much cheaper. In both cases the traveler must conform to the schedule of the transport. Furthermore, the traveler is limited to designated points along a route. Buses usually offer more complete coverage of a city than trains. Trains may provide much quicker transport between distant points, however.

Deciding on the Type of Transport to be Used

The location of the objective of travel will dictate whether it is to be reached by foot or by use of public transport, and if by public transport which option should be used. Therefore, the first thing the traveler must do is to determine the location of the destination. A telephone call to the objective of travel may ascertain its location in relation to the nearest intersection. If it is not accessible by walking, the traveler should call the local transit office to determine if it can be reached by bus, train, or a combination of both.

Use of City Buses

Buses travel along given routes. Several routes may crisscross a city, providing fairly comprehensive coverage. Often, buses stop only at designated locations along the route. Bus stops are typically located just before an intersection or well after one.

Buses may line up from corner to corner at central stops and transfer points, however. Bus stops may be designated by signs, shelters, benches, or paint (Wacker, 1990). At times they are designated by location only (e.g., bus will stop just before any intersection along its route). They will almost always be located so that the passengers disembark onto the sidewalk away from the street (rather than on an island in the middle of the street).

Planning the Trip

A fair amount of pre-planning may be required when using city buses. The traveler needs to identify the bus or buses which can be used to travel from the nearest appropriate bus stop to the bus stop nearest the desired location. He also needs to be prepared to travel from that bus stop to the objective and back to a point where a return bus can be caught.

The traveler may gain route information by calling the transit company and telling the person on the phone

(a)   where he will be starting his travels from,
(b)   where he wishes to go, and
(c)   the time of day he plans to be traveling.

The dispatcher can then tell him

(a)   where to catch the bus,
(b)   the number or name of the bus to catch,
(c)   the time(s) to catch it,
(d)   if a transfer is required (if so where to get that), and
(e)   the location of the stop nearest to the destination (LaGrow & LaDuke, 1990).

It is often useful to provide periodic training to appropriate transit staff to ensure the success of this strategy.

Routes and times of departure may vary during the course of the day (i.e., in relation to rush hour or peak use). Furthermore, buses going to the same destination from a given bus stop may have slightly different routes designated by suffixes or other means. For example, one should not assume that the Massey A (via Albert) and the Massey D (direct) will always depart at the same time or travel along the same route. Routes may also vary periodically in relation to changing traffic or use patterns. Therefore, the traveler needs to be cautious when generalizing across designations, times and time of day.

Boarding and Traveling by Bus

Before boarding a bus, the traveler should confirm with the driver that

(a)   this is the desired bus, designating it by name (name, number and suffix), and

(b)   it goes to the bus stop of choice (usually designated by intersection name).

Once on the bus, the traveler pays the driver, asks to be told when the destination has been reached, and then takes a seat near the door. The traveler may ask the driver if the seat across from him by the door is empty. Often if it is taken, the passenger in it will vacate it or offer it for the use of the blind traveler. This and the one behind it are the most desirable seats on the bus for a traveler who must rely on the driver to call out his stop, since the driver is reminded of the traveler's presence each time he faces the door to let more passengers on.

Passengers may pay using a monthly pass or other multi-ride ticket or by cash. Many transit systems require the traveler to have the correct change. Some systems provide transfers if the traveler must change buses to reach his destination. In this case it is up to the traveler to request the transfer upon boarding.

When boarding the bus, the traveler uses a modified diagonal technique and the handrail. When moving about the bus, the traveler may use a shortened touch technique. He may also wish to use the vertical and horizontal rails available in many buses. If this is done, the traveler may choose to use a modified diagonal technique instead. When disembarking from the bus, the railing and an extended diagonal cane technique is utilized to ensure safety.

Maintaining Orientation

The passenger can usually keep track of the direction of travel as the bus moves along the street. However, orientation may be reconfirmed when disembarking by asking the driver

(a)   which direction the bus is facing,

(b)   the name of the street the bus is currently traveling along, and

(c)   the direction of the desired intersecting street (in front of or behind the bus).

Directional corner information may be developed using this information. For example, in countries where traffic flows along the right side of the street, the traveler will know that he is on the east, north, west, or south side of a street when disembarking from a north, west, south or east-bound bus respectively. He will also know which side of the intersecting street he is on according to the direction of travel of the bus.

Thus, if disembarking from an east-bound bus before the intersection, he would be located on the southwest corner of that intersection. If disembarking after the intersection, he would be on the southeast corner.

Instructional Strategies

Boarding, movement within the bus and disembarking may be awkward at first. Therefore instructors will often arrange to have at least one lesson at the bus depot (barn or garage), where an empty unit may be used for exploration and to practise getting on and off. The student may also benefit from a lesson designed to allow for repeated approaches to buses as they arrive at a central location. In this fashion, students may gain a degree of skill and confidence in locating the bus and the door before they are required to do so for travel purposes.

Bus travel may be introduced anywhere within the travel sequence following the successful use of the touch or constant-contact technique in outdoor environments. However, it is usually introduced after the student begins to travel in business environments. In fact, it is often not introduced until the home base for business lessons has been shifted to a central bus stop. This is done to isolate bus travel from business travel as a means of reducing anxiety in the initial lessons.

Recovery Strategies

Buses generally travel on closed routes. Therefore, they will eventually return to the point at which they were boarded. A traveler who becomes disoriented while traveling, misses his stop or cannot find a return bus can decide to continue on the route until he eventually returns to his point of origin. Likewise, the focal point of a bus system may be used to develop a city-wide recovery strategy. In this case, all buses will eventually pass through a central location. Therefore, any bus could be boarded and ridden to the focal point. The traveler would then disembark and use his knowledge of the area to reorient himself and/or catch the appropriate bus. The usefulness of this strategy is dependent upon the degree to which the traveler is familiar with the environment immediately surrounding the focal point. Fortunately, the focal point of most bus systems is in the heart of the central business district. As a result, it could be used as the home-base for business lessons.

Use of Trains, Subways and Rapid Rail Systems

Train travel is by its very nature linear. Train systems may operate at, above (elevated) or below (subway) the ground level. Trains are usually accessed from stations and boarded from platforms. Trains typically stop at each station along the way. The stops may or may not be announced. If unannounced (or unintelligible), the traveler must keep track by counting the number of stops. In either case, travelers need not sit in any particular seat to remind someone to call the stop. Therefore, any seat handy to the door would be desirable.

Trains are often boarded from an elevated platform. In this case the student should be taught to approach the edge of the platform directly (i.e., perpendicular to it) using a touch, a touch-and-slide or a constant-contact technique. When the edge has been contacted, the traveler may wish to move back from the edge a few steps and wait for the train to arrive. When traveling along the platform it may be best to utilize the constant-contact technique (Wiener, 1990).

Often someone is available to provide assistance with boarding. However, independent boarding is possible (Wiener, 1990). The traveler may trail a train positioned directly next to the platform using a modified three-point touch technique to find the door. The door and the break between cars are distinguishable from one another both tactually and auditorially by an experienced traveler. Trains which must be boarded from the track level can be trailed auditorially and/or by hand if necessary.

Transport by train is usually paid for in advance at a turnstile or a ticket counter. When a ticket is sold, it is usually collected after the train has departed from the station.

Planning the Trip

Trains stop at a few specified stations rather than numerous stops as buses do. As a result, the planning for the train ride itself is somewhat simpler. However, the complexity and irregularity of station design requires the traveler to attend to a number of important details when planning a trip. First of all, the traveler needs to determine

(a)   the location of the station where the train will be boarded,
(b)   the location of turnstiles or ticket booths,
(c)   where the train will be found (e.g., number of floors up or down from the station entrance or turnstile to the platform used for boarding the train),
(d)   where to go on reaching the platform,
(e)   if it is a single or double-track platform, and
(f)   if a double-track platform, on which side of the platform the train will be found.

Likewise, when exiting, the traveler needs to know

(a)   which side of the train the doors will open,
(b)   which direction to turn to find the exit,
(c)   the location of the exit (e.g, number of floors up or down from the platform), and
(d)   the point where the exit meets the street (Bentzen, 1990; Wiener, 1990).

Travel must then be planned from that point to the desired destination .

If it can be reached on foot, the student will have to plan the trip from the station to the objective keeping directional corner information in mind. Attention must be given to crossing busy streets. The traveler may find it helpful to contact local government departments, such as public works or traffic engineering to find out 'where the destination sought is in relation to the [station exit or] bus stop, whether there are sidewalks along all the streets to be traveled, and if there is any street or road repair underway. Travelers can usually find out how many blocks they must travel in any given direction to reach their destination. In addition, the department of traffic engineering (or other relevant office) can be called to determine where traffic or pedestrian lights are located along any particular route, what the relative volume of traffic on the streets is like, whether the streets are one-way or two-way, and, if they are one-way, the direction in which traffic flows' (LaGrow & LaDuke, 1990, p. 134).

Locating and Boarding the Train

Trains are typically boarded from platforms raised above the track and the traveler must be aware of the danger of an edge when traveling in these environments (Mueller & Stone, 1990).

Platforms may be single or double edged. If double edged, the traveler must find out which way to turn upon entering the platform. The edge of the platform should be approached perpendicularly, using a constant-contact technique. Edges are often marked by a textural change. Once the edge has been located, the traveler should remain well back and wait for the train to arrive. When entering the train, the traveler listens for the opening door and people entering and leaving the train. The door opening should be located with the cane and the height of the floor determined before stepping from the platform onto the train (and off the train and onto the platform when exiting) (Wiener, 1990).

Instructional Strategies

Students usually benefit from both generalized instruction for travel on trains and platforms and environmentally specific instruction for the various platforms and stations used. The transit environment poses a number of hazards to the traveler not encountered elsewhere. Of primary concern in this environment is the ability of the student to locate the edge of the platform and avoid misadventure with it (Mueller & Stone, 1990).

Training usually begins in a relatively quiet station with a simple layout, where the student may practice locating turnstiles, platforms, and the platform edge. Emphasis is placed on environmental regularities, auditory clues, perpendicular alignment, the use of constant-contact techniques and the identification of visual and tactile markings which indicate the presence of the edge.

As with bus travel, students are typically introduced to trains parked in a barn or station and provided with an opportunity to approach, board and explore the car while others are not using it. Practice is provided in this environment until the student has demonstrated the ability to consistently identify the door opening and discriminate between it and the dangerous void between cars.

Students are introduced to increasingly complex stations as they gain skill and experience. Some stations consist of a single platform located directly through the turnstile. More complex environments may have a number of staircases or escalators leading to various track levels with platforms serving trains traveling in different directions (Eames & Eames, 1990); thus requiring environmentally specific instruction or well developed solicitation skills.

Generalization across stations requires a great deal of practice and experience. The traveler is not always able to predict the side of the train the doors will open on when exiting or if the platform alighted on will be a single or double-track platform. Also the location of stairs, turnstiles and the exit to the street is not necessarily known (Eames & Eames, 1990).

Recovery Strategies

Like bus travelers, train users need strategies to recover when lost, confused or disoriented. One of the most basic of recovery strategies a traveler can use is to telephone those who are expecting him and let them know where he is. Therefore phone skills and money handling are important. The ability to identify current location is also important. Strategies include:

(a)   going to a manned booth or store within the station or going to the street and walking to a known location, store or intersection,

(b)   reading station signs, street signs and store names if possible, and/or

(c)   identifying landmarks and clues enabling the person phoned to identify the caller's location.

Another basic strategy is to go to a known location and start again. Trains often terminate at a central station in the heart of a city. If this is the case, the traveler could get on the next train through and eventually end up in the central station. If he missed his stop or got on the wrong train, he could simply get off and return to his stop or the point of origin.

A third strategy is to identify a source of help (e.g., police, firemen, station personnel) and seek assistance. Learning to use the directions provided by such individuals will permit recovery from a lost situation. Role playing and practising of this skill is important to ensure success.

ADVOCATING FOR THE USER OF PUBLIC TRANSIT SYSTEMS

The lack of uniformity within transit systems create major problems for visually impaired travelers (Bentzen, 1990; Corn, 1990; Eames & Eames, 1990; Wiener, 1990; Uslan, 1990a). The position of bus stops may vary throughout the environment, as will markers designating the stops. The location of platforms, exits, stairs, turnstiles, rest rooms, telephones and ticket booths varies from station to station. Even the side of the train a door will open on, and the direction the traveler should turn after stepping onto the platform cannot be predicted when exiting from a train and entering an unfamiliar station.

Uniformity Throughout the Transit System

The consumer cannot expect to have all the problems created by lack of uniformity within the system corrected. Many of these problems exist because of the physical environment and variations in station, bus and train design over the years. However, some of the problems that exist can be changed system-wide and therefore should be addressed. For example, the location of bus stops can be made predictable throughout the system. Bus stops are designated by signs, paint, location and benches or shelters. The designation can be made uniform (and hopefully discernible to visually impaired persons) throughout the system. One of the simplest solutions is to have the vehicle stop before every intersection along its route to pick up waiting passengers. In this way the location of the bus stop is predictable and as easily discernible (i.e., by nature of its location) to the visually impaired traveler as to anyone else. Likewise, the location of the 'special fare' turnstile used in trains and subway stations can be made uniform throughout the system as can the type of turnstile or ticket dispenser used.

Visually impaired travelers and their advocates should stress the importance of creating and maintaining uniformity across the system whenever possible. However, many of the problems faced by the visually impaired traveler would cease to exist if relevant and timely information was available (Uslan, 1990a). Therefore, an equal amount of energy should be put into improving communication throughout the system.

Improved Communication

The transit system communicates with its customers by sign, printed schedules and maps, public announcements and by transit personnel in response to enquiry. Signs need to convey relevant information, carry a simple message and be visible to the public. Signs may be used to designate the specific bus or train to be boarded, indicate the names and numbers of buses which stop at a given place, the direction to various platforms within a station, the direction the train will travel, the side of the platform the train will arrive on, and the location of the street, the phones, and rest rooms, among other things. The visibility of signs is extremely important to a traveler's overall success with the use of the system. The visibility of signs is enhanced if they are produced in large print with high contrast materials, and are mounted on the wall at eye level in a well lit area (Corn, 1990; Eames & Eames, 1990; Manzer & Chew, 1990). Electronic signs used to designate buses and trains may also be produced in a large print, high-contrast format, thus increasing their visibility (Provost-Hatlen & Myers, 1990).

Schedules and maps used to convey route information should be produced in the simplest form which still conveys the needed information. They may be produced for personal use as pamphlets and/or mounted on the wall for public perusal. In both cases they are easier to read if they are produced in large print with good contrast. Maps and schedules produced for public use should be prominently displayed in well lit, non-glare areas, which are accessible for close examination by the traveler (Uslan, 1990a).

Tactile maps may also be used to display route information. 'Tactile transit maps should contain at least the following information: the lines of the system, the location of each station stop in the system, and the name of each station' (Bentzen, 1990, p. 64).

Announcements made over public address systems within the station and by intercom within the train or bus should be clear and concise (Eames & Eames, 1990; Uslan, 1990a). The latter could indicate the side of the train the door will open on and the direction to turn to exit when reaching the platform in addition to the name of the stop, if relevant.

The information received from transit personnel may be of utmost importance when planning a trip which requires the use of public transportation. The traveler may phone the transit office seeking specific information. When using buses, the traveler needs to know which bus he should board, where to board it, the direction it will be travelling when boarding and disembarking, where to disembark, if a transfer is needed and where the return bus can be caught (LaGrow & LaDuke, 1990). Similar information is needed when traveling by train (see Bentzen, 1990). The quality of the information provided is crucial and can be improved, if necessary, through the provision of in-service training (Provost-Hatlen & Myers, 1990).

One of the most efficient ways of advocating for the needs of visually impaired travelers and helping to improve communications within the transit system is through the provision of quality in-service training programs provided to transit personnel. Programs can be conducted to increase sensitivity of the staff to the needs of visually impaired travelers while providing training in the specific skills needed to meet those needs (e.g., human guide techniques and dealing with requests for specific route information over the phone) (Eames & Eames, 1990; LaGrow & LaDuke, 1990; Provost-Hatlen & Myers, 1990; Uslan, 1990b).

Definitions and Terminology

Although definitions may vary, the ones presented here express our meaning and understanding of a term.

Orientation and Mobility

Orientation and mobility is a term which refers to both

(a)   the techniques and strategies required for independent travel by blind and visually impaired people, and

(b)   the success-based sequence of instruction used to promote independent travel among blind and visually impaired persons.

Orientation

Orientation refers to the process involved in monitoring one's position in space through the use of the senses and in relation to the known patterns of environments to facilitate purposeful movement. As a result, one can be oriented, disoriented and become reoriented. Being oriented implies that one knows where one is, where one wishes to go, and how to get there.

Orientation has been defined as the 'process of utilizing the remaining senses in establishing one's position and relationship to all other significant objects in one's environment' (Hill & Ponder, 1976, p. 114).

Mobility

Mobility refers to the act of movement within the physical environment. Mobility has been defined as the 'capacity, the readiness and the facility to move' (Hill & Ponder, 1976, p. 114). Mobility may be facilitated by the use of both primary and secondary mobility techniques and/or travel aids.

Primary Mobility Techniques and Travel Aids

Primary mobility techniques provide complete protection and coverage to the non-visual traveler. Primary techniques include the use of a human guide, dog guide and the constant contact and touch techniques with a specially prescribed cane.

Electronic travel aids (ETA) may also be classified as primary and secondary aids. The Laser Cane is the only ETA which qualifies as a primary aid.

Human guide techniques

Human guide consists of a group of techniques designed to utilize another person as an aid for independent mobility.

Dog guide

Dog guides are a primary mobility aid operating under the direction of the traveler. Information is relayed from the dog to the traveler by means of a rigid U-shaped harness. The dog is trained to respond to the commands of left, right and forward. They stop at curbs and steps and will avoid overhangs and obstacles in the path of travel (Whitstock, 1980).

Touch technique

The touch technique utilizes a swinging arc of the cane which tests the ground before the foot is placed on it. This technique protects both sides of the body equally and picks up drop-offs. The touch technique provides about a one-meter warning of drop-offs and will contact anything within its arc from the waist down.

Constant-contact technique

The constant-contact technique is a variant of the touch technique. The procedures are the same except that the cane is not lifted from the ground at any point in its arc.

Laser cane

The laser cane is essentially a long cane with built-in secondary electronic detection capabilities for distant early warning. This device emits three lasers aimed at the ground in front of the traveler, waist height and head height. The device will pick up any object in its path at waist and head height within 2 to 4 meters, and will indicate any dramatic increase in the distance to the ground in front of the traveler. When combined with the touch technique it may be used as a primary mobility aid, like any other long cane.

Secondary Mobility Techniques and Travel Aids

Secondary mobility techniques and travel aids do not provide complete coverage and protection from the environment. As a result, they must be used in addition to a primary technique or aid for travel in uncontrolled environments. Secondary mobility techniques include self-protective and directional techniques and the diagonal cane technique. All ETAs, other than the laser cane are secondary aids and therefore must be used in conjunction with primary devices.

Self-protective and directional techniques

Self-protective techniques include the upper-hand-and-forearm and the lower-hand-and-forearm techniques. These procedures protect the body midline at head-height and waist-height respectively. They are used in controlled indoor environments or in conjunction with primary aids for selective purposes. The directional techniques of squaring off and direction taking are used to establish or maintain a line of travel. They provide no protection from the environment.

Diagonal cane technique

The diagonal cane technique employs a long cane held diagonally across the body in a static position. This procedure protects the width of the body, but is inadequate for detecting drop-offs. As a result, it is used primarily in controlled indoor environments or in conjunction with other primary aids (e.g., human guide). It may be considered a primary technique by certain low-vision travelers.

Electronic travel aids

ETAs are used to provide supplementary information to the traveler, rather than provide protection from the environment. These devices 'detect and locate objects, provide information that allows the user to determine range, direction, dimension and height of objects' (Farmer, 1980, p. 372).

Independent Travel

Independent travel refers to the act of travelling under one's own direction and by one's own volition. One may facilitate independence while relying on others (e.g., the use of human guide or the solicitation of locational information).

Independence exists along a continuum and can be situational. As a result, one can be an independent traveler in familiar indoor environments, semi-independent in familiar outdoor environments and a rote route traveler in unfamiliar indoor and outdoor environments.

Independent traveler

Independent travel is the highest level of functioning to be obtained. The independent traveler may be required to conceptualize the environment, generalize across environments of varying complexity, interact effectively with the public, identify objectives of travel, pinpoint the objectives position and plan a route to reach it, as well as choosing alternative routes when necessary.

Semi-independent traveler

The semi-independent traveler is taught routes for travel from place to place, but is expected to generalize skills from route to route. Semi-independent travelers use recovery strategies when lost or disoriented, and may detour if necessary.

Route traveler

Individuals with the most limited abilities can often gain independence in some situations. A route traveler learns a specific route to and from a given destination. This route is repeated each time without deviation. These persons are also referred to as rote route travelers.

References

Apple, L. (1976). Orientation and mobility of patients with low vision. In E.E. Faye (Ed.), *Clinical Low Vision,* (pp. 137-142). Boston: Little, Brown & Co.

Apple, M.M., Apple, L.E., & Blasch, D. (1980). *Low Vision.* In R.L. Welsch and B.B. Blasch (Eds), *Foundations of Orientation and Mobility.* New York: American Foundation for the Blind.

Beggs, W. (1992). Coping, adjustment, and mobility-related feelings of newly visually impaired young adults. *Journal of Visual Impairment and Blindness, 86,* 136-140.

Bentzen, B. (1990). Adaptations for an accessible transit system. In M. Uslan, A. Peck, W. Wiener, & A. Stern (Eds), *Access to Mass Transit for Blind and Visually Impaired Travelers,* (pp. 61-64). New York: American Foundation for the Blind.

Blasch, B., & De l'Aune, W. (1992). A computer profile of mobility coverage and a safety index. *Journal of Visual Impairment and Blindness,* 86, 249-254.

Blasch, B., Long, R., & Griffen-Shirley, N. (1989). Result of a national survey of electronic travel aid use. *Journal of Visual Impairment and Blindness, 83,* 449-453

Bosbach, S.R. (1988). Precane mobility devices. *Journal of Visual Impairment and Blindness, 82,* 338-339.

202 ~~~~~~~~~~~~~~~~~~~~~~~~~~~~ *Orientation and Mobility*

Bryan, W.H. (1989). Itinerant orientation and mobility in public schools. *Journal of Visual Impairment and Blindness, 83,* 473-474.

Chen, D., & Smith, J. (1992). Developing orientation and mobility skills in students who are multiply impaired. *Review, 24,* 133-139.

Corn, A. (1990). The challenges of mass transit. In M. Uslan, A. Peck, W. Wiener, & A. Stern (Eds), *Access to Mass Transit for Blind and Visually Impaired Travelers,* (pp. 13-18). New York: American Foundation for the Blind.

Dale, B. (1992). Issues in traumatic blindness. *Journal of Visual Impairment and Blindness, 86,* 140-143.

Dodds, A., & Davis, D. (1989). Assessment of low vision clients for mobility. *Journal of Visual Impairment and Blindness, 83,* 439-446.

Dumas, A., & Sadowsky, A. (1984). A family training program for adventitiously blinded and low vision veterans. *Journal of Visual Impairment and Blindness, 78,* 408-414.

Eames, E., & Eames, T.G. (1990). Getting around in a major metropolis: The experiences of guide dog users in mass transit. In M. Uslan, A. Peck, W. Wiener, & A. Stern (Eds), *Access to Mass Transit for Blind and Visually Impaired Travelers,* (pp. 19-25). New York: American Foundation for the Blind.

Elliott, J.L., & Kuyk, T.K. (1992). Evaluation of the Wayne Walsh Safe-T-Lite Cane. *Journal of Visual Impairment and Blindness, 86,* 373-375.

Farmer, L. (1980). Mobility devices. In R.L. Welsh and B.B. Blasch (Eds), *Foundations of Orientation and Mobility,* (pp. 357-412). New York: American Foundation for the Blind.

Fisk, S. (1986). Constant-contact technique with a modified tip: A new alternative for long-cane mobility. *Journal of Visual Impairment and Blindness, 80,* 999-1000.

Florence, I. & LaGrow, S. (1989). The use of a recorded message for gaining assistance with street crossings for deaf-blind travelers. *Journal of Visual Impairment and Blindness, 83,* 471-472.

Foy, C.J., Kirchner, D., & Wople, L. (1991). The Connecticut Pre-cane. *Journal of Visual Impairment and Blindness, 88,* 85-86.

Foy, C.J., Von Scheden, M., & Waiculous, J. (1992). The connecticut Pre-cane: Case study and curriculum. *Journal of Visual Impairment and Blindness, 86,* 178-181.

Franck, L. (1990). Effect of cane with microprism reflecting tape on the night time visibility of blind rural travelers. *Journal of Visual Impairment and Blindness, 84,* 8-10.

Gee, K., Harrell, R., & Rosenberg, R. (1987). Teaching orientation and mobility skills within and across natural opportunities for travel: A model designed for learners with multiple severe disabilities. In L. Goetz, D. Guess, & K. Streniel-Campbell (Eds). *Innovative Program Design for Individuals with Dual Sensory Impairments,* (pp. 127-157). Baltimore: MD: Paul H. Brookes.

Guth, Hill & Reiser (1989). Tests of blind pedestrians' use of traffic sounds for street crossing alignment. *Journal of Visual Impairment and Blindness, 83,* 461-468

Hall, A., Bailey, I., Kekelis, L. Raasch, T., & Goodrich, G. (1987). Retrospective survey to investigate use of distance magnifiers for travel. *Journal of Visual Impairment and Blindness, 81,* 423-428.

Harley, R.K., & Merbler, J.B. (1980). Development of an orientation and mobility program for multiply impaired low vision children. *Journal of Visual Impairment and Blindness, 74,* 9-14.

Harley, R.K., Long, R.G., Merbler, J.B., & Wood, T.A. (1987). Orientation and mobility for the blind multiply handicapped young child. *Journal of Visual Impairment and Blindness, 81,* 377-381.

Harley, R.K., Wood, T.A., & Merbler, J.B. (1980). An orientation and mobility program for multiply impaired blind children. *Exceptional Children, 46,* 326-331.

Hill, E.W. (1984). The role of the orientation and mobility instructor in the public schools. In G.T. Scholl (Ed.). *Quality services for blind and visually handicapped learners: Statement of position.* Reston, VA: ERIC Clearinghouse on Handicapped and Gifted Children, Council for Exceptional Children.

Hill, E.W., Dodson-Burk, B., & Smith, B. (1989). Orientation and mobility for infants who are visually impaired. *RE:VIEW, 21,* 47-60.

Hill, M.M., & Hill, E.E. (1991). Provision of high-quality orientation and mobility services to older persons with visual impairments. *Journal of Visual Impairment and Blindness, 85,* 402-408.

Hill, E., & Ponder, P. (1976). *Orientation and Mobility Techniques: A Guide for the Practitioner.* New York: American Foundation for the Blind.

Hill, E.W., Rosen, J., Correa, V.I., & Langley, M.B. (1984). Preschool orientation and mobility: An expanded definition. *Education of the Visually Handicapped, 16,* 58-72.

Joffee, E. (1989). Developing orientation and mobility services for severely and profoundly retarded students in the New York city public schools. *Long Cane News, 8*(1), 3-4.

Joffee, E. & Rikhye, C. (1991). Orientation and mobility for students with severe visual and multiple impairments: A new perspective. *Journal of Visual Impairment and Blindness, 85,* 211-216.

Ketterer, H. (1988). Mobility begins at birth: An early childhood orientation and mobility readiness program. In N. Neustadt-Noy, S. Merin, & Y. Schiff (Eds), *Orientation and Mobility of the Visually Impaired,* (pp. 101-108). Jerusalem, Israel: Heiliger.

Kronick, M.K. (1987). Children and canes: An adoptive approach. *Journal of Visual Impairment and Blindness, 81,* 61-62.

LaGrow, S. (1989). Behavioral strategies commonly employed in orientation and mobility instruction. *Orientation and Mobility Instructors Association Journal, 7* (1), 7-9.

LaGrow, S. (1990). Shaping and fading: Procedures used to teach the skills required for independent travel. *Orientation and Mobility Instructors Association of Australasia Journal, 8* (2), 4-11.

LaGrow, S. (1992). *Rehabilitation of Visually Impaired People.* Auckland: Royal New Zealand Foundation for the Blind.

LaGrow, S., & Blasch, B. (1992). Orientation and mobility services for older persons. In A.L. Orr (Ed.), *Vision and Aging: Crossroads for Service Delivery.* New York: American Foundation for the Blind.

LaGrow, S., & LaDuke, R. (1990). A three-pronged plan for soliciting travel information. In M. Uslan, A. Peck, W. Wiener,

& A. Stern (Eds), *Access to Mass Transit for Blind and Visually Impaired Travelers,* (pp. 128-135). New York: American Foundation for the Blind.

LaGrow, S., & Leung, J.P. (1990). Behavioral strategies employed with visually impaired individuals. *Advances in Special Education, 7B,* 111-113.

LaGrow, S., Wiener, W., & LaDuke, R. (1990). Independent travel for developmentally disabled persons: A comprehensive model of instruction. *Research in Developmental Disabilities, 11,* 289-301.

Long, R., McNeal, L., & Griffin-Shirley, N. (1990). *The Effect of Visual Loss on Mobility of Elderly Persons.* Final report, National Institute on Disability and Rehabilitation Research Grant No. 133 GH 70038.

Long, R.G., Rieser, J.J., & Hill, E.W. (1990). Mobility in individuals with moderate visual impairments. *Journal of Visual Impairment and Blindness, 84,* 111-118.

Manzer, D. & Chew, K. (1990). Light rapid and light rail systems in western Canada. In M. Uslan, A. Peck, W. Wiener, & A. Stern (Eds), *Access to Mass Transit for Blind and Visually Impaired Travelers,* (pp. 57-61). New York: American Foundation for the Blind.

Mishkin, A. (1988). The family's psychological challenge in adjusting to a blind or sight-impaired member. In N. Neustadt-Noy, S. Merin, & Y. Schiff (Eds), *Orientation and Mobility of the Visually Impaired.* Jerusalem, Israel: Heiliger Publishing Co.

Moore, J. (1984). Impact of family attitudes toward blindness/ visual impairment on the rehabilitation process. *Journal of Visual Impairment and Blindness, 78,* 100-105.

Mueller, D. & Stone, E. (1990). A step-by-step program for using orientation and mobility techniques. In M. Uslan, A. Peck, W. Wiener, & A. Stern (Eds), *Access to Mass Transit for Blind and Visually Impaired Travelers,* (pp. 104-111). New York: American Foundation for the Blind.

Pereira, L.M. (1990). Spatial concepts and balance performance: Motor learning in blind and visually impaired children. *Journal of Visual Impairment and Blindness, 84,* 109-111.

Pogrund, R.I., & Rosen, S.J. (1989). The preschool blind child can be a cane user. *Journal of Visual Impairment and Blindness, 83,* 431-438.

Ponchillia, P. (1984). Family services: Role of the center-based teaching professional. *Journal of Visual Impairment and Blindness, 78,* 97-100.

Provost-Hatlen, T. & Myers, L.A. (1990). Advocating in behalf of blind and visually impaired bus travelers. In M. Uslan, A. Peck, W. Wiener, & A. Stern (Eds), *Access to Mass Transit for Blind and Visually Impaired Travelers,* (pp. 87-91). New York: American Foundation for the Blind.

Rikhye, C., Gothelf, C., & Appell, M. (1989). A classroom environment checklist for students with dual sensory impairments. *Teaching Exceptional Children, 22,* 44-46.

Rowland, C., & Schweight, P. (1990). *Tangible Symbol Systems: Symbolic Communications for Individuals with Multi-Sensory Impairments.* Tucson, AZ: Communication Skill Builders.

Skellinger, A.C., & Hill, E.W. (1991). Current practices and considerations regarding long cane instruction with preschool children. *Journal of Visual Impairment and Blindness, 85,* 101-104.

Smith, A., De l'Aune, W., & Geruschat, D. (1992). Low vision mobility problems: Perceptions of orientation and mobility specialists and persons with low vision. *Journal of Visual Impairment and Blindness, 86,* 58-62.

Straw, L., Harley, R., & Zimmerman, G. (1991). A program in orientation and mobility for visually impaired persons over age 60. *Journal of Visual Impairment and Blindness, 85,* 108-113.

Sulzer-Azaroff, B., & Mayer, G.R. (1991). *Behavior Analysis for Lasting Change.* New York: Holt, Rinehart and Winston.

Taheri-Araghi, M. (1992). Visually impaired people in Iran: Cultural and environmental effects on orientation and mobility services. *Journal of Visual Impairment and Blindness, 86,* 151-152.

Thomson, C., Brown, T., Chapman, J., Benson, A., & Pine, T. (1991). *Individualised Educational Planning: A Guide for Meeting Learners' NeEds* Palmerston North, New Zealand: Massey University Press.

Uslan, M., & Schreibman, K. (1980). Drop-off detection in the touch technique. *Journal of Visual Impairment and Blindness, 74,* 179-182.

Uslan, M. (1990a). Blind and visually impaired travelers in mass transit: An overview. In M. Uslan, A. Peck, W. Wiener, & A. Stern (Eds), *Access to Mass Transit for Blind and Visually Impaired Travelers,* (pp. 4-11). New York: American Foundation for the Blind.

Uslan, M. (1990b). In-service training for bus drivers. In M. Uslan, A. Peck, W. Wiener, & A. Stern (Eds), *Access to Mass Transit for Blind and Visually Impaired Travelers,* (pp. 91-93). New York: American Foundation for the Blind.

Uslan, M., Hill, E., & Peck, A. (1989). The profession of orientation and mobility in the 1980s: The AFB competency study. New York: American Foundation for the Blind.

Vander Kolk, C. (1981). *Assessment and Planning with the Visually Impaired.* Baltimore: University Park Press.

Wacker, C. (1990). Teaching blind and visually impaired riders about an urban bus system. In M. Uslan, A. Peck, W. Wiener, & A. Stern (Eds), *Access to Mass Transit for Blind and Visually Impaired Travelers,* (pp. 116-123). New York: American Foundation for the Blind.

Ward, M.E. (1986). Planning the individualized education program. In G.T. Scholl (Ed.), *Foundations of Education for Blind and Visually Handicapped Children and Youth: Theory and Practice,* (pp. 215-238). New York: American Foundation for the Blind.

Welsh, R. (1980). Visually impaired older persons. In R. Welsh and B. Blasch (Eds), *Foundations of Orientation and Mobility,* (pp. 420-428). New York: American Foundation for the Blind.

Whitstock, R. (1980). Dog guides. In R.L. Welsh and B.B. Blasch (Eds), *Foundations of Orientation and Mobility,* (pp. 565-580). New York: American Foundation for the Blind.

Wiener, W.R., & Welsch, R.L. (1980). The profession of orientation and mobility. In R.L. Welsch and B.B. Blasch (Eds). *Foundations of Orientation and Mobility.* New York: American Foundation for the blind.

Wiener, W.R. (1992). Orientation and mobility, In AFB's *Accomodation and Accessibility: Implementing the ADA on a Local Level.* (pp. 14-16). New York: American Foundation for the Blind.

Wiener, W. (1990). Training for travel in rapid rail. In M. Uslan, A. Peck, W. Wiener, & A. Stern (Eds), *Access to Mass Transit for Blind and Visually Impaired Travelers,* (27-30). New York: American Foundation for the Blind.

Wright, K. (1972). The rehabilitation process. In R.E Hardy and J.G. Cull (Eds) *Social and Rehabilitation Services for the Blind* (pp. 207-217). Springfield, IL: Charles C. Thomas.

About the Authors

Steven J. LaGrow received his B S in Sociology in 1975, his M A in Blind Rehabilitation in 1976 from Western Michigan University, and his Ed.D in special education from Northern Illinois University in 1982. He has worked as an orientation and mobility specialist with children and adults in both center and community-based programs. He has published a number of papers on various aspects of orientation and mobility instruction including: systematic strategies for deaf-blind travelers to acquire assistance for street crossings, and systems for teaching mentally retarded travelers foot and bus travel. He is past president of the Orientation and Mobility Instructors' Association of Australasia and has served on a number of international committees including the International Committees of Division Nine (Orientation and Mobility) of the Association for the Education and Rehabilitation of Blind and Visually Impaired People. He is currently the Professor and Head of Rehabilitation Studies at Massey University, Palmerston North, New Zealand.

Marvin J. Weessies received his BS degree in Business Education from Western Michigan University in 1964 and his MA in Orientation and Mobility in 1964. He was supervisor of Orientation and Mobility Services at the Vision Enrichment Center in Grand Rapids, Michigan until 1970. He joined the faculty of the Department of Blind Rehabilitation and Mobility at Western Michigan University in the fall of 1970 and continues there as an Associate Professor.